101 SONGS FOR EASY GUITAR BOOK 2

Wise Publications
London/New York/Sydney

Music Sales Limited
8/9 Frith Street, London, W1V 5TZ, England.
Music Sales Pty. Limited
120 Rothschild Avenue, Rosebery, NSW 2018, Australia.

This book © Copyright 1979 by
Wise Publications
ISBN 0.86001.609.9
Order No. AM 23540

Compilation & Design: Pearce Marchbank and Jane Coke

Wise Publications
London/New York/Sydney

Music Sales complete catalogue lists thousands
of titles and is free from your local music
book shop, or direct from Music Sales Limited.
Please send a cheque or postal order for £1.50 for postage to
Music Sales Limited, 8/9 Frith Street, London, W1V 5TZ, England.

Printed and bound in Malta by Interprint Limited

Rainy Day, Dream Away
Words and music by Jimi Hendrix

Moderate Funky Blues

Rain-y day,— dream a-way,— Let the sun take a hol-i-day.

Flow-ers bathe and see the chil-dren— play Lay back and groove on a

rain-y day. Well, I can see a bunch of wet preach-ers; look at 'em on the run! The

car-ni-val traf-fic noise, It sinks to a splash-y hum.— E-ven the ducks can groove,

rain bat-ter-ing in the park-side pool, And I'm lean-ing on my win-dow sill —

dig-ging ev-'ry-thing!— (And-uh you, too.)

The Wind Cries Mary
Words and music by Jimi Hendrix

sweep- ing   up   the   bro -ken   piec - es   of   yes -ter - day's____

life.   Some where   a   queen   is   weep-ing,   Some -

where _____ a   King ___ has   no   wife,   And the

wind   it   cries _____ Ma - ry.

The   traf - fic lights they turn   blue   to -

2. The traffic lights they turn blue tomorrow   Will the wind ever remember
    And shine their emptiness down on my bed;   The names it has blown in the past,
    The tiny island sags downstream   And with this crutch, its old age and its wisdom
    'Cos the life that they lived is dead.   It whispers, "No, this will be the last."
    And the wind screams Mary.   And The Wind Cries Mary.

Spanish Castle Magic
Words and music by Jimi Hendrix

if you   want to   go,   *You know it's*

a really   groovy place, and it's just a little   bit   of   Spanish Castle Magic.

(Sung) It's

Verse 2: The clouds are really low
          And they overflow
          With cotton candy
          And battle grounds
          Red and brown.
          But it's all in your mind
          Don't think your time
          On bad things.
          Just float your little mind around
          Look out.

Chorus 2:

          Hang on, my darling, yeah
          Hang on if you want to go
          It puts everything else on the shelf
          With just a little bit of Spanish Castle Magic
          Just a little bit of daydream here and there.

Foxy Lady
Words and music by Jimi Hendrix

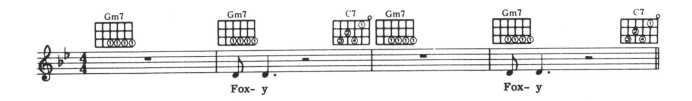

Fox- y   Fox- y

You know— you are a   cute lit-tle heart break-er. —   Fox-y   yeah,

And you know— you are a   sweet lit-tle love mak-er, —   Fox-y.

I wan-na take you home,   yeah,   I won't do you no harm. —

You've got to be all   mine, — all mine,   ooh Fox- y lad-y.

Fox-y   Fox-y, Now- a I see you ___ come

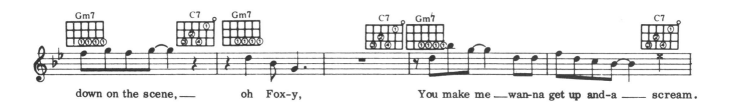

down on the scene, ___ oh Fox-y,   You make me ___ wan-na get up and-a ___ scream.

Fox-y, oh baby list-en now,   I've made up my mind, ___ I'm tired of wasting all my

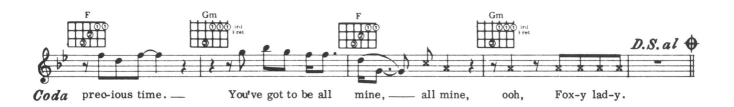

Coda prec-ious time. ___   You've got to be all   mine, ___ all mine,   ooh,   Fox-y lad-y.

D.S. al ⊕

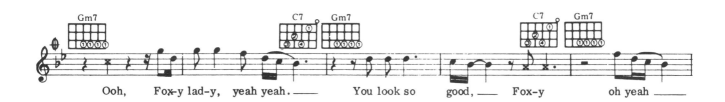

Ooh, Fox-y lad-y, yeah yeah. ___   You look so   good, ___ Fox-y   oh yeah ___

Fox-y   yeah,   give us some, Fox-y,   Fox· y   Fox- y.

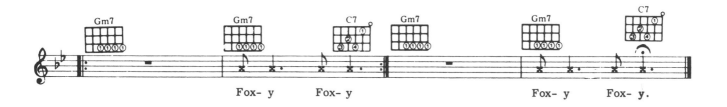

Fox- y   Fox- y   Fox- y   Fox- y.

Long Hot Summer Night

Words and music by Jimi Hendrix

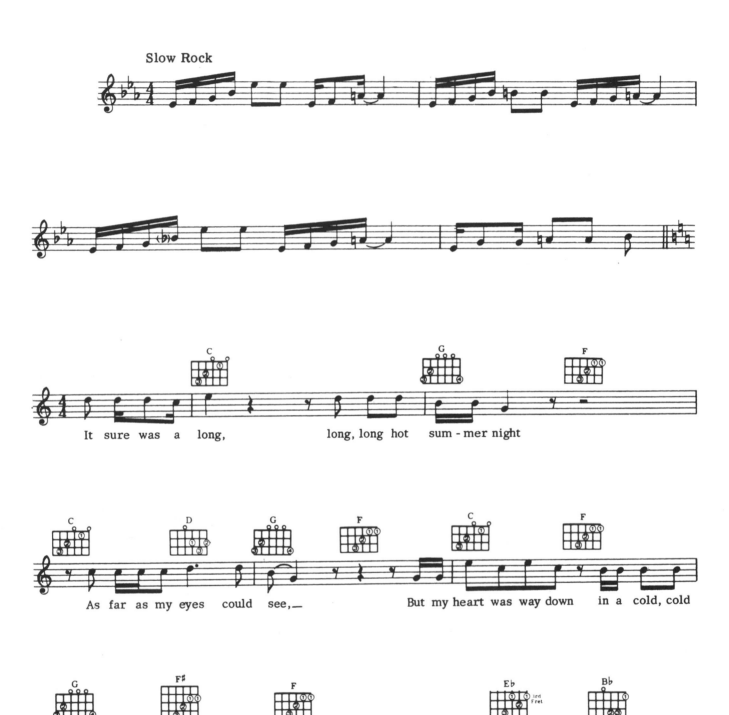

It sure was a long, long, long hot sum-mer night

As far as my eyes could see,— But my heart was way down in a cold, cold

win-ter storm. Oh my dar-ling, where can you be?

round a-bout this time the tel-e-phone__ blew its horn a-cross the room,

Scared lit-tle An-nie clean out__ of her mind._____

(Roman the candle, he peeps out of his peek-a-boo, hide and seek) And

grabs lit-tle An-nie from the ceil-ing just in time.__

And the tel-e-phone keeps on scream-in'.__

Yeh, yeh, yeh, yeh, "Hel-

lo", said my shak-y voice__ "Well how you do-ing?" (I start to stutter uh, uh)

"Can't you tell I'm do-ing fine?"___ It was my ba-by talk-ing and she's way down 'cross the bor-der. She says "I'm goin' to hur-ry to you, I've been a fool and I'm tired_of cry'n." It was a long, long hot sum-mer night As far as my eyes could see___ But I can feel the heat com-in' on as my ba-by's get-tin' clos-er. I'm so glad that my ba-by's com-in' to res-cue me. So glad that my ba-by's com-in' to res-cue me.

Machine Gun

Music by Jimi Hendrix

Remember

Words and music by Jimi Hendrix

Oh, re - mem-ber the mock-ing bird, my ba - by bun, He used to
mem-ber the blue - birds and the hon - ey bees, They used to

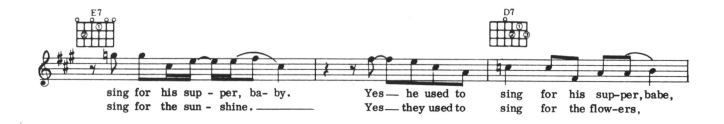

sing for his sup - per, ba - by. Yes — he used to sing for his sup-per, babe,
sing for the sun - shine. _____ Yes — they used to sing for the flow-ers,

He used to sing so sweet _____ since my ba - by left me he
They used to sing so sweet, _____ But- a since my ba - by left me they

ain't sang in two long days. 1. Oh, _____ re - 2.

Hey! pret-ty ba-by, come on back to me. Make ev-'ry-bod-y hap-py as can be. _____ So

ba-by, if you'll please come home a-gain you know I'll kiss you for my sup-per, You know I'll

kiss you for my din-ner, babe, yeah! But-a if you don't come
back you know I'll have to starve to death 'Cos I

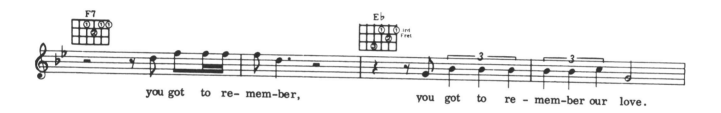

ain't had one kiss all day ——— now. Please ── re - mem-ber,

you got to re- mem-ber, you got to re - mem-ber our love.

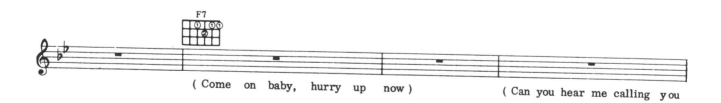

Come on back. come on back in my arms, ——— I'll make ev-'ry-thing that bet-ter.

(Come on baby, hurry up now) (Can you hear me calling you

fade

back again now?) (Come on baby, stop jiving around) (Hurry home — hurry home)

Bold As Love

Words and music by Jimi Hendrix

Slowly, with a beat

An - ger he smiles, tow-'ring in shin-y met - al - lic pur-ple ar - mor, Queen

Jeal-ous - y, en - vy waits be-hind him, Her fie-ry green gown sneers at the gras-sy ground,

Blue are the life giv-ing wa-ters tak-ing for grant - ed, They qui-et - ly un-der-stand.

Once hap-py Tur-quoise arm-ies lay op-po-site read-y, but won-der why the fight is on.

But they're all Bold As Love.___ But they're all Bold As Love.___

But they're all Bold As Love, Just ask the Ax-is.

My Red is so confident
He flashes trophies of war and ribbons of euphoria
Orange is young, full of daring
But very unsteady for the first go round
My Yellow in this case is not so mellow
In fact, I'm trying to say that it's frightened like me.

And all these emotions of mine
Keep holding me from giving my life to a rainbow like you
But I'm, yeah, I'm as Bold As Love
But I'm as Bold As Love
But I'm as Bold As Love
Just ask the Axis, he knows everything.

Pop Star

Words and music by Cat Stevens

Fairly bright tempo

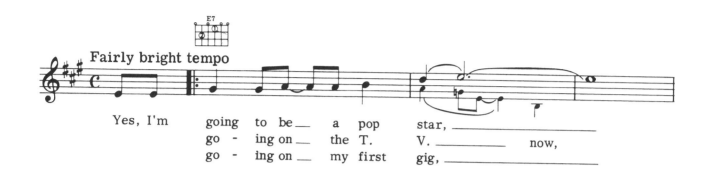

Yes, I'm going to be __ a pop star, _____
go - ing on __ the T. V. _____ now,
go - ing on __ my first gig, _____

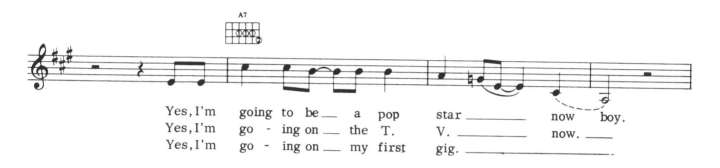

Yes, I'm going to be __ a pop star _____ now boy.
Yes, I'm go - ing on __ the T. V. _____ now. ____
Yes, I'm go - ing on __ my first gig. _____

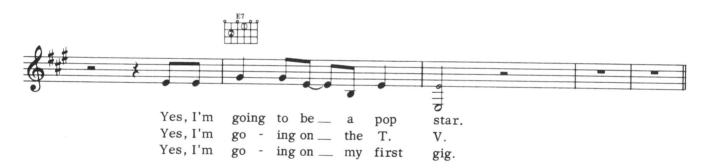

Yes, I'm going to be __ a pop star.
Yes, I'm go - ing on __ the T. V.
Yes, I'm go - ing on __ my first gig.

Oh ma - ma ma - ma see __ me, Ma-ma, ma-ma see me, I'm a pop star.
Oh ma - ma ma - ma see __ me, Ma-ma, ma-ma see me on the T. V.
Oh ma - ma ma - ma see __ me, Ma-ma, ma-ma see me on my first gig.

2 Yes, I'm
3 Yes, I'm

Now list-en to me.

Da na da da_ na da na __ na da da_ na va   da na va da_ na da   da.

Da na da da _ na da na __ na da da_ na va   da na va da na da na   da.

Da na da da _ na   da na __ na da da_ na da   da na va da da na da   da

da   da na da da na da na.   da na.   Well, I'm go - ing to_ the cold

bank, ___ cold bank,_   Yes, I'm go - ing to_ the cold bank ___ now,_

___   Yes, I'm go - ing to_ the cold bank.   Oh ma - ma,

ma - ma see — me, Ma-ma, ma-ma see me at the cold bank. ____

Well, I'm com - ing, com - ing, com-ing home ____ now. ____

Yes, I'm com - ing, com - ing, com-ing home ____ now. ____

Yes, I'm com - ing, com - ing, com - ing home now.

Oh ma - ma, ma - ma see — me, Ma-ma, ma-ma see me, I'm home.

Hard Headed Woman

Words and music by Cat Stevens

Slow beat

I'm look-ing for a hard head-ed wo-man,

One who'll take me for __ my - self, __ And if I find my hard head-ed

wo - man, __ I won't need __ no-bod-y else, No, no, no. _____

__ I'm look-ing for a hard head-ed wo-man, One who will make me do __ my

best. __ And if I find my hard head-ed wo - man, __

I know the rest of my life __ will be blessed, Yes, yes, yes. _____

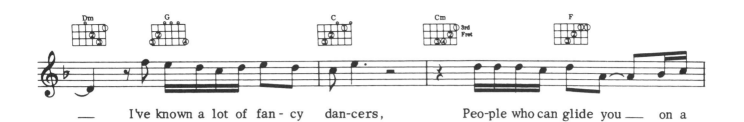

— I've known a lot of fan - cy dan-cers, Peo-ple who can glide you __ on a

floor, _____ They move so smooth _ but have no an - swer. _

When you ask _____ what d'you come here for, why?

I know ma-ny fine feath-ered friends, ___ But their
They know ma-ny sure - fire ways _____ To find

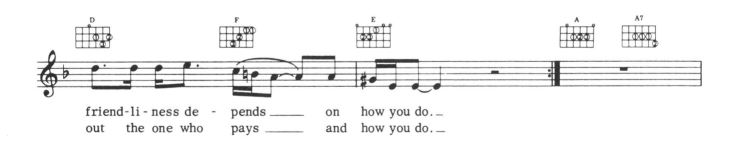

friend-li-ness de - pends _____ on how you do. _
out the one who pays _____ and how you do. _

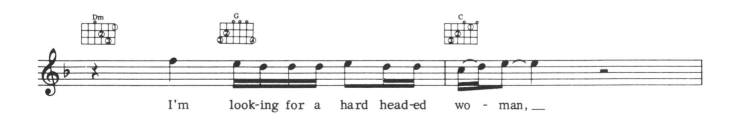

I'm look-ing for a hard head-ed wo - man, __

Moon Shadow
Words and music by Cat Stevens

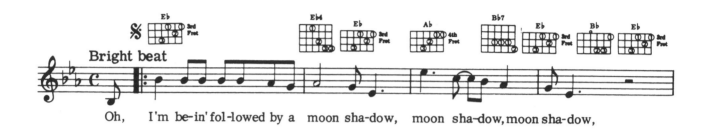

Bright beat

Oh, I'm be-in' fol-lowed by a moon sha-dow, moon sha-dow, moon sha-dow,

Leap-in' and hop - pin' on a moon sha-dow, moon sha-dow, moon sha-dow, _____ And

1 if I ev - er lose_ my hands,_ lose my power,_ lose_____ my hands,_ Oh
2 if I ev - er lose_ my legs _____ I won't moon,_ and I ___ won't beg, ___ Oh

if I ev - er lose_ my hands,_ Ooh _____ I
if I ev - er lose_ my legs,_ Ooh _____ I

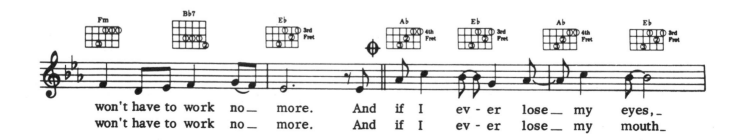

won't have to work no_ more. And if I ev - er lose_ my eyes,_
won't have to work no_ more. And if I ev - er lose_ my mouth_

26

If my col - our all ___ runs dry, ___ Yes if I ev - er lose___
And my teeth ___ North ___ or South, ___ Yes if I ev - er lose___

___ my eyes, Ooh _____ I won't have to cry no___
___ my mouth, Ooh _____ I

more. Yes won't have to talk. Did it take long to find___

___ me? I asked the faith - ful light___ Did it take long to find___

D.% al ⊕

___ me, ___ And are you gon - na stay___ the night. ___ Oh

Coda

moon sha - dow, moon sha - dow, Moon sha - dow, moon sha - dow.

Let It Bleed

Words and music by Mick Jagger and Keith Richard

Medium

CHORUS

Well we all ___ need some - one ___ we can lean on ___
need some - one ___ we can dream on ___

And if you want it, well you can lean on me. ___
And if you want it, well you can dream on me. ___

Well, we all ___ need some - one ___ we can lean on ___
Yeah we all ___ need some - one ___ we can cream on ___

And if you want it well you can lean on me. ___
And if you want to well you can cream on me. ___

1. She said "My breasts they will al - ways be op - en
2. (-) I was dream-ing of ___ a steel ___ gui-tar en-gage ___ ment

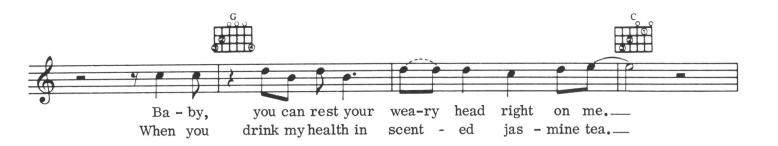

Ba - by, you can rest your wea-ry head right on me. —
When you drink my health in scent - ed jas - mine tea. —

And there will al - ways be a space in my parking lot
(- -) You knifed me in my — dir -ty fil - thy basement —

When you need — a lit-tle coke and sym - pa -thy. ————
With that ja - ded fa-ded jun-ky nurse, oh what pleasant com - pa-ny. —

CHORUS

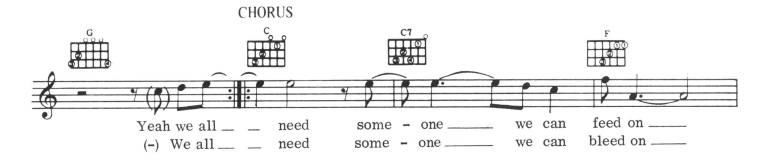

Yeah we all — — need some - one ——— we can feed on ———
(-) We all — — need some - one ——— we can bleed on ———

And if you want it well you can feed on me. —
And if you want it why don't you bleed on me. —

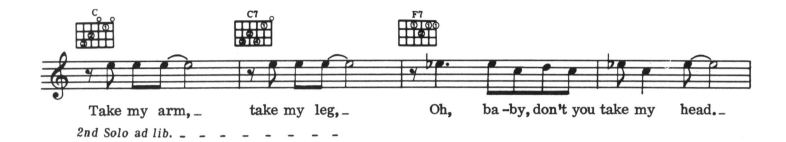

Take my arm, _ take my leg, _ Oh, ba-by, don't you take my head. _

2nd Solo ad lib. _ _ _ _ _ _ _ _

We all __ need some-one we can b-

-leed on __ And if you want it, ba - by, well you can bleed on me. _

1st time only

We all __ __Get it on, ri - der__ Get it on, ri - der__

repeat ad lib. to fadeout

Get it on, __ ri - der __ you can bleed all o - ver me. __
You can be my ri - der __ you can bleed all o - ver me. __

Do You Feel Like We Do

Words and music by Peter Frampton, Rick Wills,
John Headley-Down and Mick Gallagher

1. Woke up this morn-ing with a wine glass in my hand.

Whose wine, what wine, where the hell did I dine?

Must have been a dream, I don't be - lieve where I've been.

Come on, let's do it a - gain.

Chorus

Do you, ___ you ___

feel like I ___ do? ___ Do you, ___ you ___

1.

___ feel like I ___ do? ___

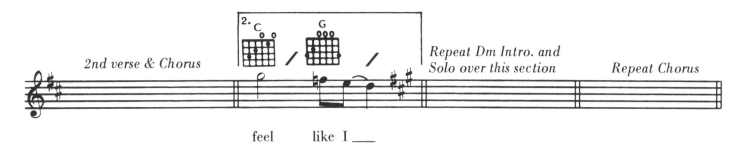

2nd verse & Chorus   Repeat Dm Intro. and
Solo over this section   Repeat Chorus

feel   like I __

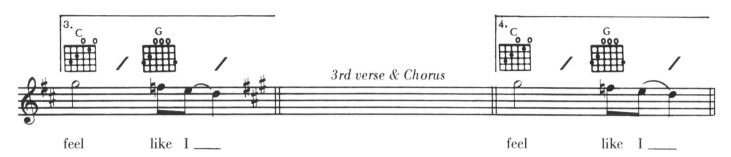

3rd verse & Chorus

feel   like I __   feel   like I __

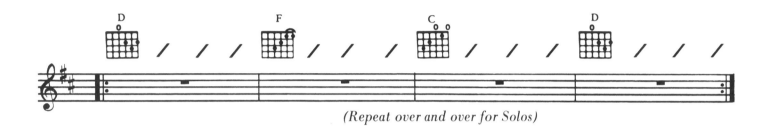

(Repeat over and over for Solos)

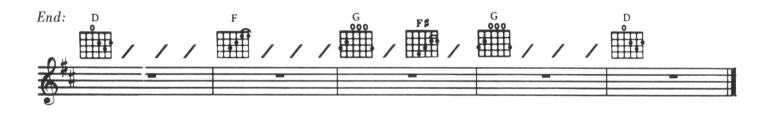

2. My friend got busted just the other day.
Don't walk, don't walk, don't walk away.
Drove into a taxi, bent the boot, hit the back.
Had to play some music, otherwise he'd crack.

Chorus: Do you feel like I do? Do you, you, feel like I . . .

3. Champagne for breakfast and a Sherman in my hand.
Peach top, peach tails, never fails.
Must have been a dream, I don't believe where I've been.
Come on, let's do it again.

Do you, you, feel like I do? Do you, you, feel like I . . .

Doo Doo Doo Doo (Heartbreaker)

Words and music by Mick Jagger and Keith Richard

The po-lice in New York ci-ty ___ chased a boy ___ right through the

park ___ And in a case ___ of mis-ta-ken I-den-ti-ty ___

they put ___ a bul-let through his heart ___ Heart breaker ___ with your

for-ty four ___ I wan-na tear ___ your world a-part ___

Heart breaker ___ with your for-ty four ___ I wan-na tear ___ your world a-

Sympathy For The Devil

Words and music by Mick Jagger and Keith Richard

Please al - low me to in - tro - duce my - self, I'm a man of wealth and

taste. I've been a - round for long, Long years stol - en

man - y a man's soul and faith. I was a - round when Je -

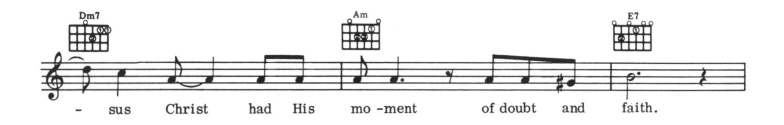

- sus Christ had His mo - ment of doubt and faith.

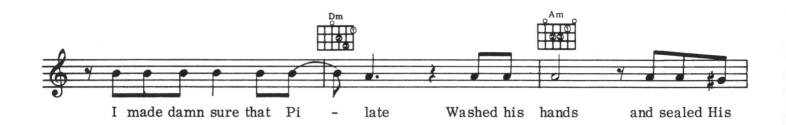

I made damn sure that Pi - late Washed his hands and sealed His

CHORUS

fate.

Pleased to meet you hope you guess my

name._____ But what's puzzling you__ is the na-ture of my game.

_____

I stuck a - round St. Pe-ters-burg when I

I watched with glee while your kings and queens fought for

saw it was time for a change__ I killed the Tzar and his

ten de-cades for the Gods they made. I shout-ed out "Who killed the

min-is-ters;__ An-as-ta-sia Screamed in vain. I

Kenned-ys?__ When af-ter all it was you and me.__

rode a tank held a gen - 'ral's rank when the blitz - krieg raged and the

Let me please in-tro-duce__ my-self I'm a man__ of wealth and

37

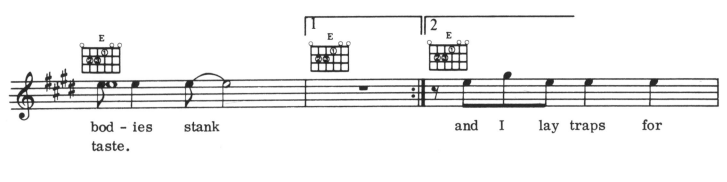

bod - ies stank and I lay traps for

taste.

trou - ba - dors who get killed be- fore they reach Bom - bay._____

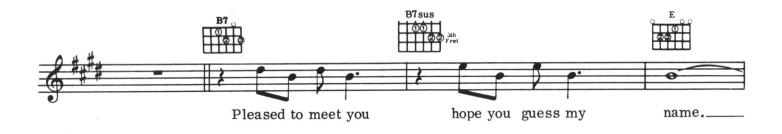

Pleased to meet you hope you guess my name._____

_____ But whats puz-zling you___ is the na- ture of my game._____

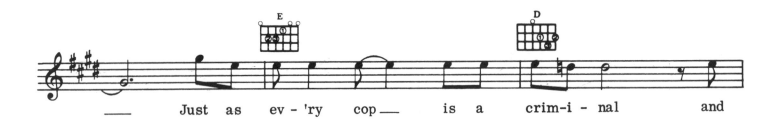

_____ Just as ev- 'ry cop ___ is a crim-i - nal and

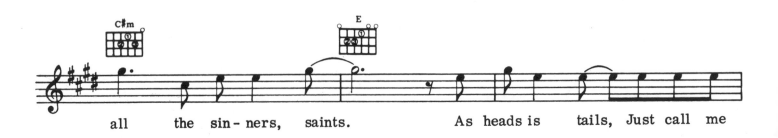

all the sin-ners, saints. As heads is tails, Just call me

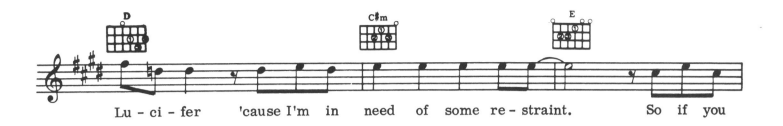

Lu - ci - fer 'cause I'm in need of some re - straint. So if you

meet me, Have some court-es - y___ have some sym-pa -thy and some

taste. Use all ___ your well ___ learned pol - i - tesse or I'll

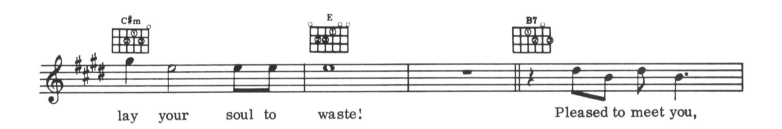

lay your soul to waste! Pleased to meet you,

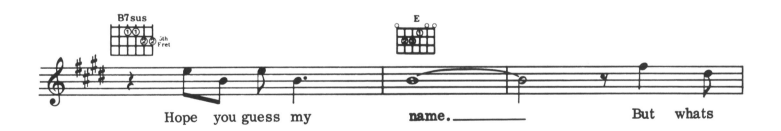

Hope you guess my name._____ But whats

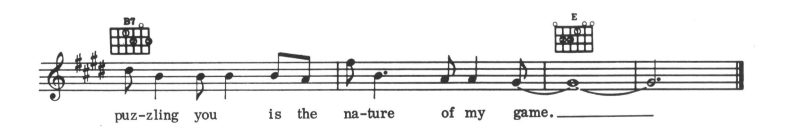

puz-zling you is the na-ture of my game._____

Get Off My Cloud

Words and music by Mick Jagger and Keith Richard

I live in an a-part-ment on the nine-ty ninth floor of my
te - le-phone is ring-in' I say "Hi it's me Who's there on the
sick and tired, fed up with this and de-cided to take a drive down

block
line?"
town.

And I sit at home look-in' out the win-dow im -
A voice says, "Hi hul-lo. How are you?""Well
It was so ve-ry quiet and peaceful.There was

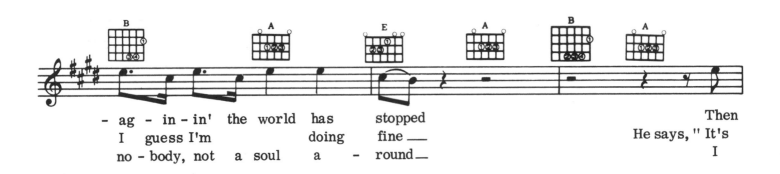

- ag - in - in' the world has stopped
I guess I'm doing fine ___
no - body, not a soul a - round ___

Then
He says, " It's
I

in flies a guy that's all dressed up just like a U - nion ___
three a. m. and there's too much noise Don't you people ev - er want to go to
laid my - self out I was so tired and I start-ed to

Midnight Rambler

Words and music by Mick Jagger and Keith Richard

Did you hear a-bout the mid-night ram - bler?   (-)
talk-ing 'bout the mid-night gam - bler,   the

ev-'ry-bo-dy got to go   Did you hear a-bout the mid-night ram-
one you ne-ver seen be-fore   (-) A-talk-ing 'bout the mid-night gam-

- bler,   (-) the one that shut the kit-chen door?   He
- bler,   did you see him jump the gar-den wall?   A-

don't give a hoot of a warn-ing   a-wrapped up in a black cat cloak.
-sigh-ing down the wind so sad-ly   a-lis-ten and you hear him moan.

(--) He don't go in the light of the morn-ing,   he's
Well I'm a-talk-ing 'bout the mid-night gam-bler,   (-)

split the time the cock-'rel crows.
ev - 'ry-bo - dy got to go.___

A -

A - did you hear a - bout the mid - night ram-

- bler?___ well ho - ney, it's no rock and roll show.   Well I'm a -

talk-ing'bout the mid-night___ ram - bler,___   yeah,   the one you ne -ver seen be-fore.___

Well you

heard a -bout the Bos-ton ___   -   it's not one of those   Well,

talk-ing 'bout the mid-night – the one who closed the bed-room door

I'm called the hit and run rape her in an - ger, the

knife-sharpened tip-py-toe, Or just the shoot 'em dead brain-bell

jang - ler, you know, the one you ne-ver seen be-fore. So if you

ev-er meet the midnight ram - bler (--) padding down your marble hall
lis-ten for the midnight ram - bler play it ea-sy sy as you go

Well he's prow-ling like a proud black pan - ther you can
I'm going to smash down all your plate glass win - dows put a

say I told you so Well won't you
fist right thru' your steel plate door,

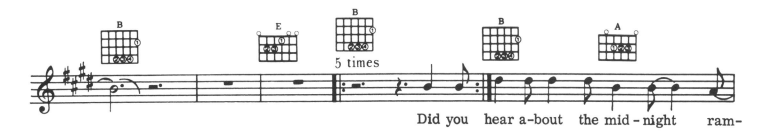

Did you hear a-bout the mid-night ram-

- bler? He'll leave his footprints up and down __ your __ hall. ____ A-did you

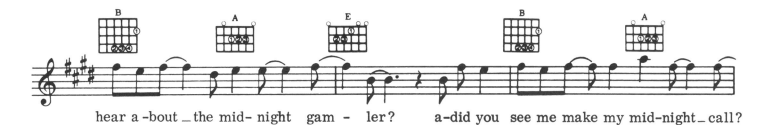

hear a-bout __ the mid-night gam - ler? a-did you see me make my mid-night __ call?

____ And if you e - ver catch __ the mid-night ram - bler, __ I'll steal __ your

mis-tress from un-der your nose. Well, go ea - sy with your cold __ fan- - dan-

- go, __ I'll stick my knife right down your __ throat, ba-by and it hurts!

Bennie And The Jets

Words and music by Elton John and Bernie Taupin

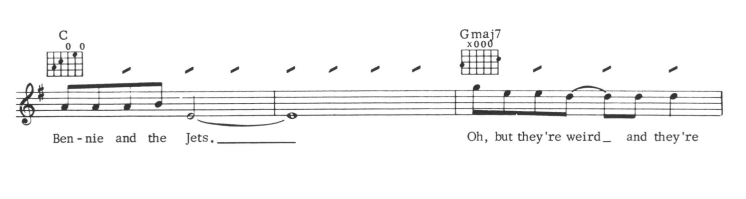

Ben - nie and the Jets._____ Oh, but they're weird_ and they're

won - der - ful, oh Ben - nie, she's real - ly keen;____ she's got e -

lec - tric boots,_ a mo-hair suit._ You know I read it in a mag-a - zine,__

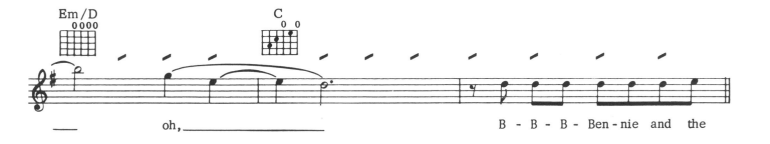

__ oh,_____ B - B - B - Ben - nie and the

Jets.

 2. *D. S. %) (instrumental)
and fade*

Tonight's The Night
Words and music by Rod Stewart

Moderately slow Rock beat

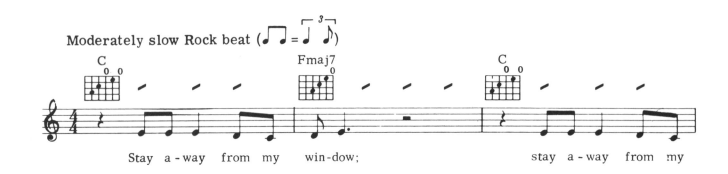

Stay a-way from my win-dow;   stay a-way from my

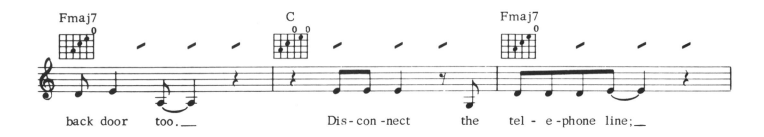

back door too.__   Dis - con -nect the tel - e -phone line;__

re - lax, ba - by,   and draw that blind.__

1. Kick off your shoes   and sit right down __

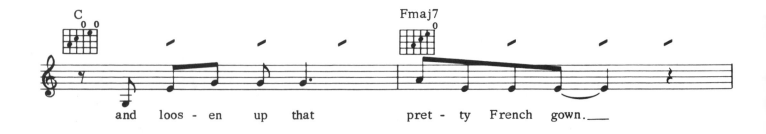

and loos - en up that   pret - ty French gown.___

Additional lyrics

2. Come on, angel, my heart's on fire;
   Don't deny your man's desire.
   You'd be a fool to stop this tide;
   Spread your wings and let me come inside.

3. Don't say a word, my virgin child;
   Just let your inhibitions run wild.
   The secret is about to unfold
   Upstairs before the night's too old.

A Boy Named Sue

Words and music by Shel Silverstein

Moderately bright

Recitative

1. Well, my daddy left home when I was three, And he didn't
2. must have thought it was quite a joke, And it got lots

leave much to Ma and me, Just this old gui - tar and an
of laughs from a lot of folks, it seems I had to fight

empty bottle of booze. Now, I don't blame him be-cause he run and hid,
my whole life thru. Some gal would gig-gle and I'd get red, And some

But the mean - est thing that he ev - er did was be-fore he
guy would laugh and I'd bust his head, I tell you, life

For Repeats   *Last time*

left, he went and named me Sue. 2. Well, he
ain't eas-y for a boy named Sue.

50

3. (Well,) I grew up quick and I grew up mean.
   My fist got hard and my wits got keen.
   Roamed from town to town to hide my shame,
   but I made me a vow to the moon and stars,
   I'd search the honky tonks and bars and kill
   that man that give me that awful name.

4. But it was Gatlinburg in mid July and I had
   just hit town and my throat was dry.
   I'd thought I'd stop and have myself a brew.
   At an old saloon on a street of mud
   And at a table dealing stud sat the dirty,
   mangy dog that named me Sue.

5. Well I knew that snake was my own sweet dad
   from a worn-out picture that my mother had.
   And I know that scar on his cheek and his evil eye.
   He was big and bent and gray and old
   And I looked at him and my blood ran cold,
   and I said, "My name is Sue. How do you do.

   Now you're gonna die." Yeah, that's what
   I told him.

6. Well I hit him right between the eyes and he
   went down, but to my surprise he come up
   with a knife
   And cut off a piece of my ear. But I busted a
   chair right across his teeth. And we
   crashed through
   The wall and into the street kicking and
   a-gouging in the mud and the blood
   and the beer.

7. I tell you I've fought tougher men but I really
   can't remember when.
   He kicked like a mule and he bit like a
   crocodile. I heard him laughin' and then
   I heard him cussin',
   He went for his gun and I pulled mine first.
   He stood there looking at me and I saw
   him smile,

8. And he said, "Son, this world is rough and if
   a man's gonna make it, he's gotta be tough
   And I know I wouldn't be there to help you
   along. So I give you that name and I
   said 'Goodbye,'
   I knew you'd have to get tough or die. And it's
   that name that helped to make you strong.

9. Yeah," he said, "now you have just fought one
   helluva fight, and I know you hate me
   and you've
   Got the right to kill me now and I wouldn't
   blame you if you do. But you ought
   to thank me
   Before I die for the gravel in your guts and the
   spit in your eye because I'm the _ _ _ _
   That named you Sue."

   Yeah, what could I do? What could I do?

10. I got all choked up and I threw down my gun.
    Called him a pa and he called me a son,
    And I come away with a different point of view.
    And I think about him now and then.
    Every time I tried, every time I win and if I
    ever have a son I think I am gonna name him
    Bill or George - anything but Sue.

Rave On

Words and music by Norman Petty, Bill Tilghman and Sunny West

Bright beat

The lit - tle things___ you say and do, ___ They
(The) way you dance ___ and hold me tight, ___ The

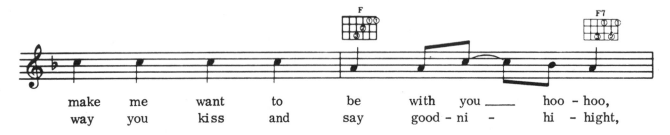

make me want to be with you ____ hoo - hoo,
way you kiss and say good - ni - hi - hight,

Rave on! It's a cra - zy feel - in' and I know it 's___

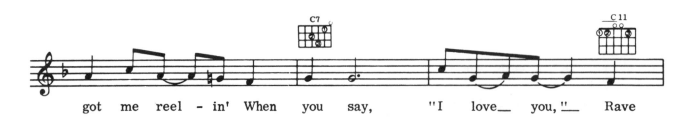

got me reel - in' When you say, "I love___ you," Rave

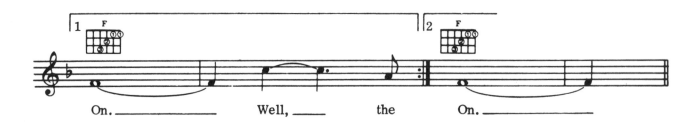

On. _____ Well, ___ the   On. _____

52

Not Fade Away

Words and music by Charles Hardin and Norman Petty

Brightly

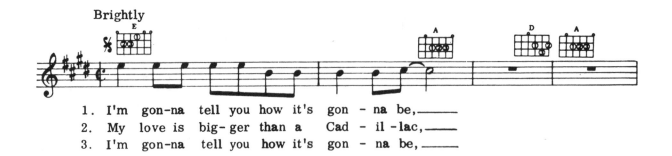

1. I'm gon-na tell you how it's gon - na be,_____
2. My love is big-ger than a Cad - il -lac,_____
3. I'm gon-na tell you how it's gon - na be,_____

You're gon-na give- a your love to me. _____
I try to show it and you drive me back. _____
You're gon-na give- a your love to me. _____

A

I wan -na love you night and day; _____
Your love for me has got to be real; _____
love to ___ last more than one day; _____

54

You know my love — not — fade a - way. —
For you to know — just — how I feel. —
A love that's love — not — fade a -way. —

Well, you know my love — not — fade a - way. —
A love for real — not — fade a - way. —
A love that's love — not — fade a - way. —

1   *Repeat, then to ℅*   **2**   *Repeat, then to ℅*

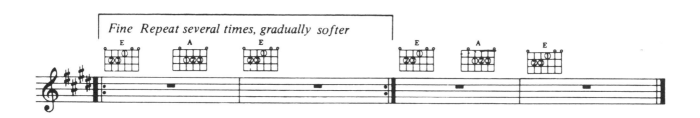

Fine Repeat several times, gradually softer

Everyday

Words and music by Charles Hardin and Norman Petty

Very brightly

Ev - 'ry Day It's a - get -tin' clos - er, Go - ing

fast - er than a roll - er - coast - er, Love like yours will

sure - ly come my way. _____

Ev - 'ry Day It's a - get - tin fast - er, Ev - 'ry - one said,

"Go on up and ask her," Love like yours will sure - ly

come my way.＿＿＿＿＿＿ Ev – 'ry day＿＿

＿ seems a lit – tle long – er, Ev – 'ry way＿＿ love's a lit – tle

strong – er, Come what may, do you ev – er long for true

love from me?＿＿＿＿ Ev – 'ry Day it's a – get – tin'

clos – er, Go – ing fast – er than a roll – er – coast – er;

Love like yours will sure – ly come my way.＿＿＿

way.＿＿＿＿＿＿＿＿

The Night They Drove Old Dixie Down

Words & Music by J. Robbie Robertson

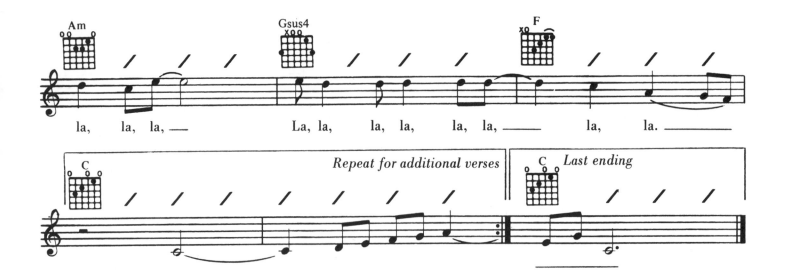

la, la, la, —— La, la, la, la, la, la, —— la, la. ——

Repeat for additional verses | Last ending

Virgil Caine is the name
And I served on the Danville train
'Til Stoneman's Cavalry came
And tore up the tracks again
In the winter of sixty-five
We were hungry, just barely alive
By May the tenth
Richmond had fell — it's a time
I remember, oh, so well

The night they drove old Dixie down
And the bells were ringin'
The night they drove old Dixie down
And the people were singin'
They went la, la, la, la, la, la
La, la , la, la, la, la, la, la

Back with my wife in Tennessee
When one day she called to me
"Virgil, quick, come see
There goes Robert E. Lee!"
Now, I don't mind choppin' wood
And I don't care if the money's no good
Just take what you need and leave the rest
But they should never have taken
The very best

The night they drove old Dixie down
And the bells were ringin'
The night they drove old Dixie down
And the people were singin'
They went la, la, la, la, la, la
La, la, la, la, la, la, la, la

Like my father before me
I will work the land
And like my brother above me
Who took a rebel stand
He was just eighteen, proud and brave
But a Yankee laid him in his grave
I swear by the mud below my feet
You can't raise a Caine back up
When he's in defeat

The night they drove old Dixie down
And the bells were ringin'
The night they drove old Dixie down
And the people were singin'
They went la, la, la, la, la, la
La, la, la, la, la, la, la, la

The night they drove old Dixie down
And the bells were ringin'
The night they drove old Dixie down
And the people were singin'
They went la, la, la, la, la, la
La, la, la, la, la, la, la, la

Fun, Fun, Fun

Words and music by Brian Wilson and Mike Love

Bright Rock-Boogie beat

1. Well, she got her dad-dy's car and she
   girls can't stand her 'cause she

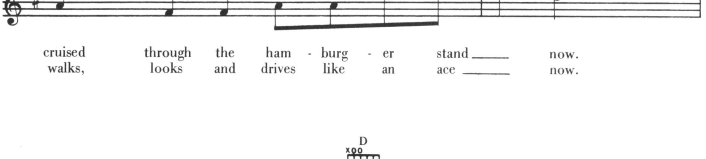

cruised through the ham-burg-er stand ___ now.
walks, looks and drives like an ace ___ now.

Seems she for-got all a-bout ___ the li
She makes the "In-dy" five hun - dred look

brar-y like she told her "old man" ___ now.
like a Ro-man char-i-ot race ___ now.

And with her ra - di - o blast - in', goes
A lot - ta guys try to catch ___ her, but she

cruis - in' just as fast as she can ___ now.)
leads 'em on a wild goose chase ___ now.)

And she'll have fun, fun, fun, till her dad - dy takes the T - bird a - way. ___

1.
2.

___ 2. Well, the

A - well, you knew all a - long ___ that your

dad was get - tin' wise to you ___ now. And since he

62

took your set of keys you've been think-in' that your fun is all through_

_____ now But you can come a-long with me, 'cause we

got-ta lot-ta things to do_____ now. And you'll have

fun, fun, fun, now that dad-dy took the T-bird a-way.____

1. And you'll have

2. And you'll have fun, fun, fun, now that

Repeat and fade

dad-dy took the T-bird a-way.____

In The City

Words and music by Paul Weller

Bricks And Mortar

Words and music by Paul Weller

Bricks and mor - tar re - flect - ing soc - ial change,__
Yel - low bull - do - zers the don - key jack - ets and

__ S. C. B's.__ While hun - dreds are home - less.
Cracks in the pave - ment re - veal

Crav - ing for suc - cess.__ Why do we try___ to hide __
They're con - struct - ing a park - ing space. Why do they have ___ to knock __

__ our past ___ by pull - ing down hous - es and build - ing car parks.
__ them down ___ and leave the site dor - mant for months on end?

Win - dows and mir - rors tell a two way glass. __ This is pro - gress, no - thing
Who has the right___ to make that choice?__ A man whose home__ has cost

stands in its path. _____ Bricks and mor - tar
for - ty grand. _____

Bricks and mor - tar, Knock 'em down!

Sounds From The Street

Words and music by Paul Weller

Non-Stop Dancing
Words and music by Paul Weller

Crest Of A Wave

Words and music by Rory Gallagher

Well you can ride on the crest of a wave if that's where you
see by the way that they are
it's a lie, it's a joke that you are

want to be but does the look on your face mean you're real-ly feel - ing
talk - ing that it's time for you to pick up your grip start
liv - ing but you know one thing they don't, you won't

hap - py or do you feel like you're standing on a wood-en leg, or a
walk - ing, 'cause they want to see your long legs fly-ing
give in, 'cause you're like a cat chas-in' its tail

poor man much too proud to beg, or a page from a book that can't be read at all
go to the place where the earth meets the sky and don't stop to turn a-round and wave good bye at all
makes a mil-lion cir - cles but you're gon-na fail look down you just don't understand

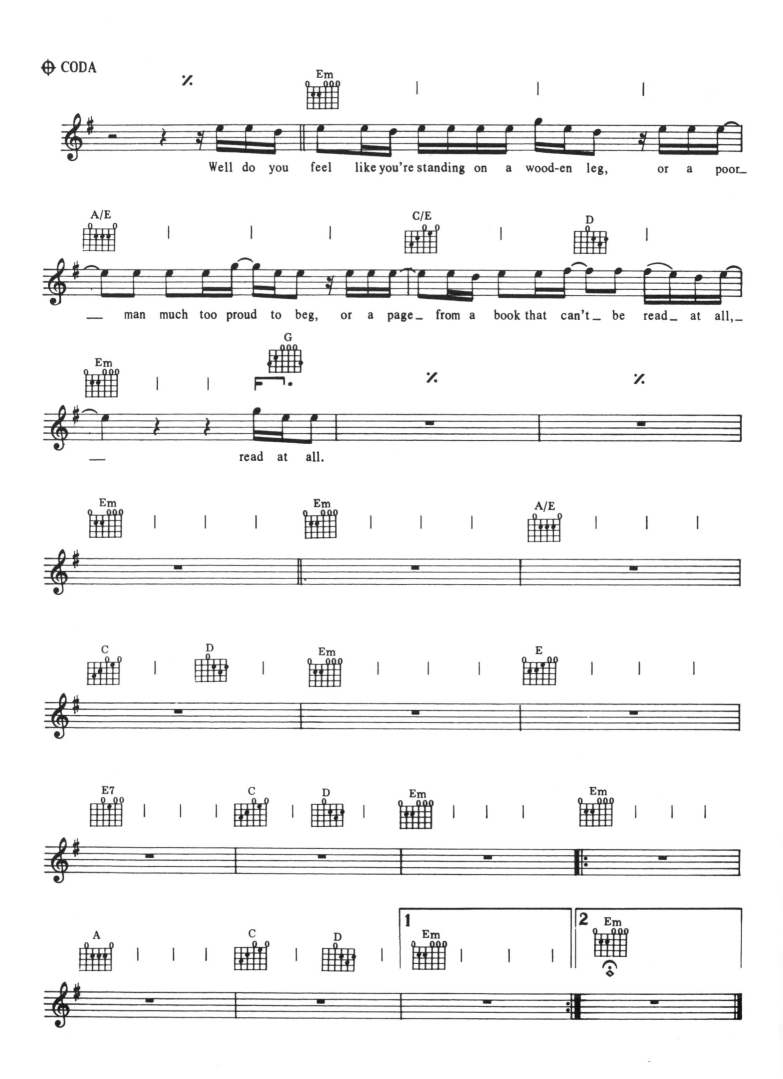

⊕ CODA

Well do you feel like you're standing on a wood-en leg, or a poor

man much too proud to beg, or a page from a book that can't be read at all,

read at all.

Show Me The Way

Words and music by Peter Frampton

Moderate Rock beat

Guitar Intro.

1. I won - der how you're feel - ing _____ there's ring - ing in __ my ears__ _____ and no one to re - late ___ to 'cept the sea. ____ Who can I __ be - lieve in?_____ I'm kneel - ing on __ the floor____ there has to be __ a force__

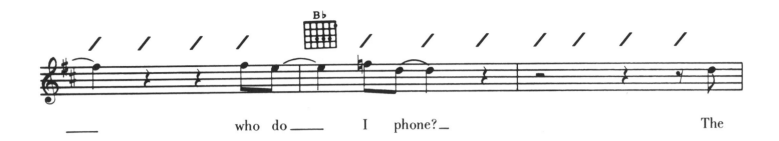

who do ___ I phone?___ The

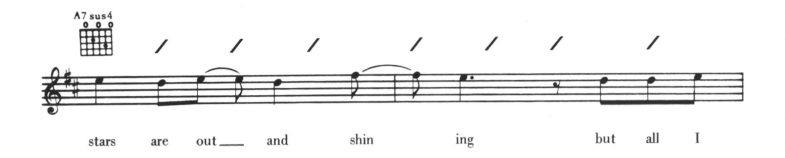

stars are out ___ and shin ing but all I

real - ly **want**___ to know, _____ Oh, won't ___

Chorus

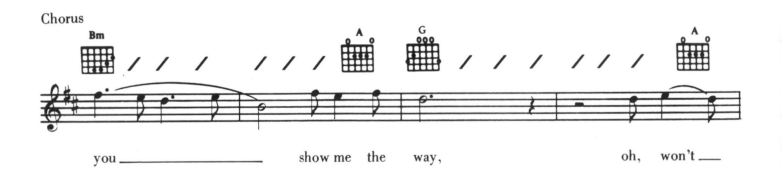

you _____ show me the way, oh, won't ___

Repeat Intro., play 2nd verse & Chorus

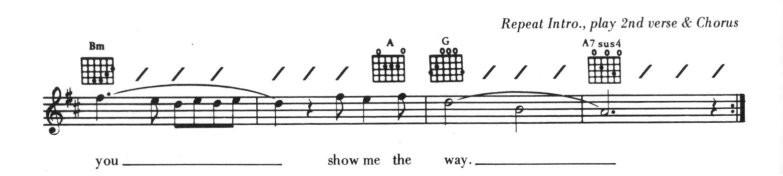

you _____ show me the way._____

3. I won-der if __ I'm dream - ing   I feel so un - a - shamed.

____ I can't be - **lieve**__ **this** is hap - pen - ing__ to

me._____ I watch you when__ you're sleep

Repeat Chorus and fade

ing and then I want to take your love._____ Oh won't

2. Well I can see no reason, you living on your nerves
   When someone drops a cup and I submerge
   I'm swimming in a circle, I feel I'm going down.
   There has to be a fool to play my part.
   Someone thought of healing but all I really want to know

2nd Chorus: Oh won't you show me the way, I want you to show me the way
I want you day after day.

3. I wonder if I'm dreaming I feel so unashamed
   I can't believe this is happening to me
   I watch you when you're sleeping, then I want to take your love

3rd Chorus: Oh won't you show me the way *(twice)*
I want you day after day *(twice)*
I want you to show me the way.

Moonchild

Words and music by Rory Gallagher

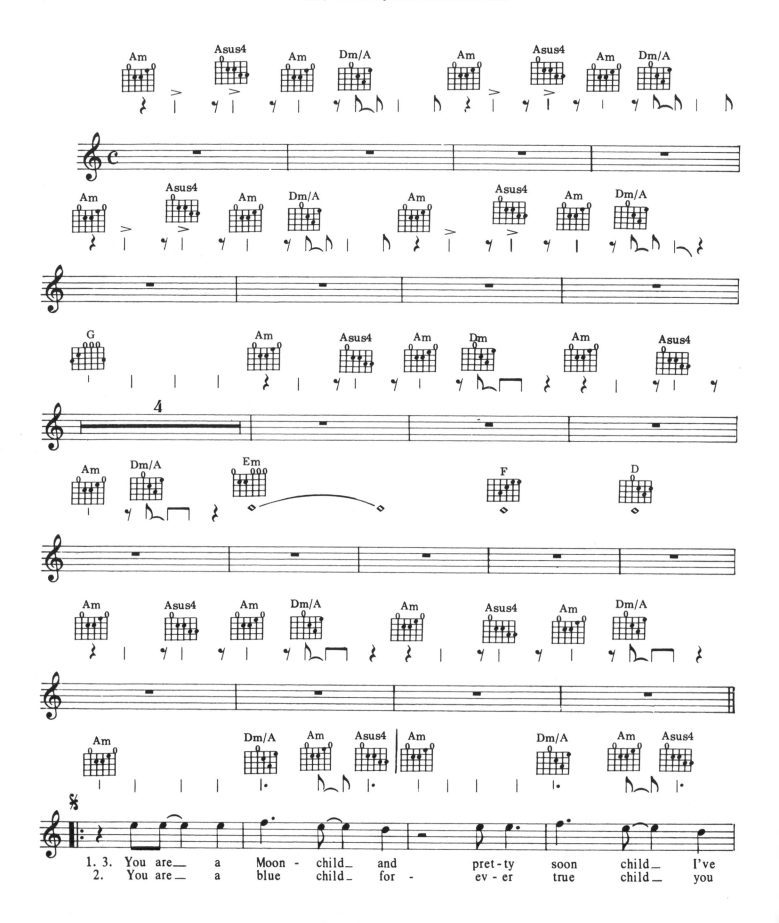

1. 3. You are__ a Moon - child__ and pret - ty soon child__ I've
2. You are__ a blue child__ for - ev - er true child__ you

got that feel - ing___ that I'm gon - na make___ you smile___ for - ev -
know that I'll try___ to paint the skies___ blue___ for - ev -

- er, If I can.
- er, If I can.

Just

give me a sign ___ and I'll ___ show you my plan ___

To Coda

Tell me why you look___ so sad ___

Time slips by like grains of sand.

Just put your fut - ure in my hands.

Solo ad lib.

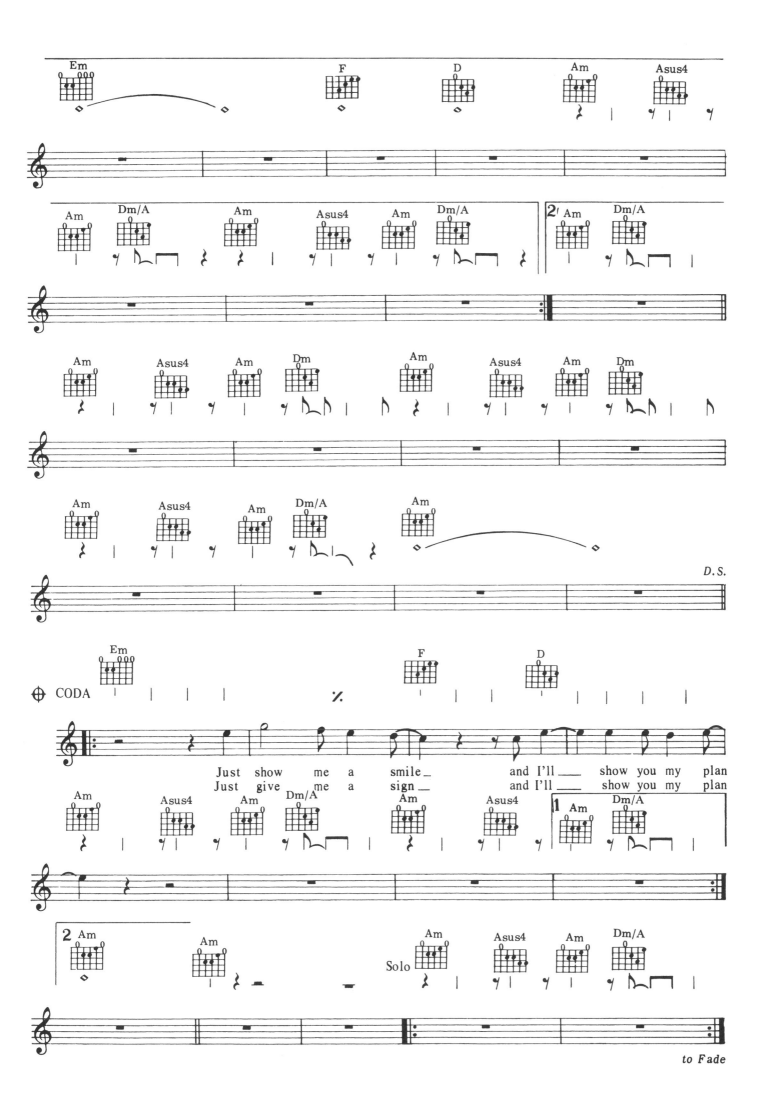

Just show me a smile___ and I'll___ show you my plan
Just give me a sign___ and I'll___ show you my plan

Race The Breeze
Words and music by Rory Gallagher

Well that
      board the
      night is
      old

sounds like the night__ train
age - ing gamb - ler
ov - er as the dawn be - gins to
eng - ine driv - er

blow - in' its __
smiles as he
nev - er stepped on the

stack,
peels,
crack,
ground,

The seal
sounds
got no

spread - ing its wings on __
off a new deck__
like a hen hatch - ing__ in a
de - gree in geog - raph-y __ but

home - ward
Then he quiet - ly
chick- - en
he's been a -

track,
deals,
shack,
round,

Ar - rived here this morn - ing won't be
hands round the ta - ble from the
late last night I think I
knows all the back lines

here for
bot - tom he slips
heard a lone - ly
eyes can hard - ly

long,
three
cry
see

As fast
watch your-self__ if you play____
heard the
don't tell this man to

as a shoot - ing star
this game__
blind owl howl - ing in a
slow down

the
'cause he

A♭

That's what them eight wheels are for.
fast - est card game on wheels come on.
moon - less sky come on.
don't know what you mean all right

E♭7

2

Come on and jump a - board__
Won't you be there when it leaves,
Won't you be there when it leaves,
Won't you be there when it leaves,

I Shot The Sheriff

Words and music by Bob Marley

Bright 4

1. 4. I shot the sher - iff, but I
2. 3. I shot the sher - iff, but I

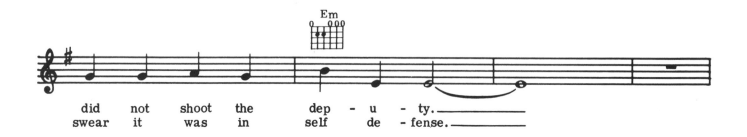

did not shoot the dep - u - ty. _____
swear it was in self de - fense. _____

I shot the sher - iff but I
I shot the sher - iff and they

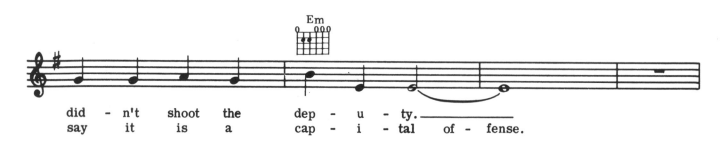

did - n't shoot the dep - u - ty. _____
say it is a cap - i - tal of - fense.

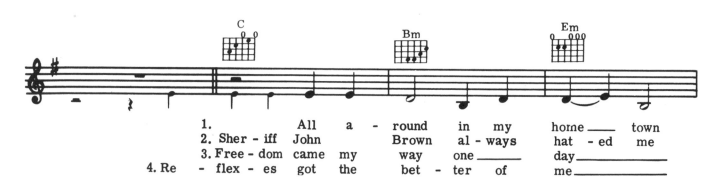

1.   All a - round in my home ___ town
2. Sher - iff John Brown al - ways hat - ed me
3. Free - dom came my way one ___ day ___
4. Re - flex - es got the bet - ter of me ___

They're try - ing to track ____ me down.
for what I don't know.
and I start - ed out ____ of town.
and what is to be ____ must be.

They say they want to bring me in guilt - ty ____
____ Ev - 'ry time that I plant a
All of a sud - den I see Sher - iff John
Ev'ry day the buck - et goes to the well, ____

for the kill - ing of a dep - u - ty. ____
seed, he said kill ____ it be - fore it ____ grow. ____
Brown ____ aim - ing to shoot me ____ down. ____
one day the bot - tom will drop ____ out.

For the life of a dep - u - ty. ____
He said kill it be - fore it ____ grow. ____
So I shot ____ I shot him down. ____
Yes, one day the bot - tom will drop ____ out. ____

1. 2. 3. **4.**
D. C. to first
verse 4 fade

But I say: ____

83

Teddy Bear

Words and music by Kal Mann and Bernie Lowe

li - on 'cause li - ons ain't the kind you love e -

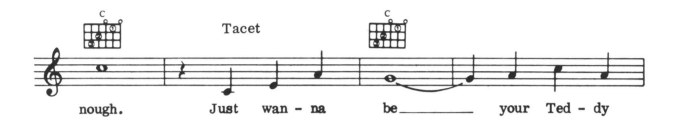

nough.   Just wan - na be_____ your Ted - dy

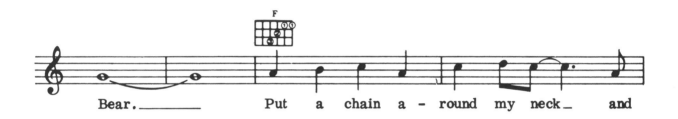

Bear._____   Put a chain a - round my neck_ and

lead me an - y - where. Oh let me be_____ your Ted-dy

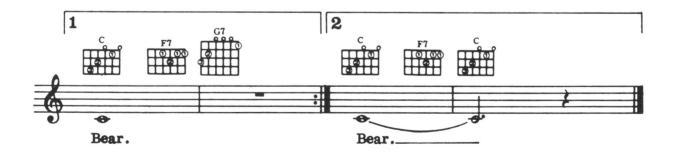

Bear.   Bear._____

My Baby Left Me

Words and music by Arthur Crudup

Moderately Bright

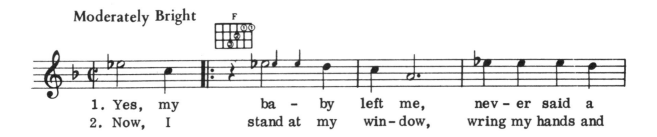

1. Yes, my ba - by left me, nev - er said a
2. Now, I stand at my win - dow, wring my hands and

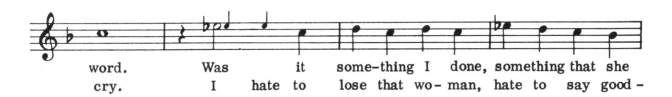

word. Was it some-thing I done, something that she
cry. I hate to lose that wo - man, hate to say good -

heard? My ba - by left me, my ba - by left me.
bye. You know she left me, yes, she____ left me.

My ba - by e - ven left me,___ nev - er said a

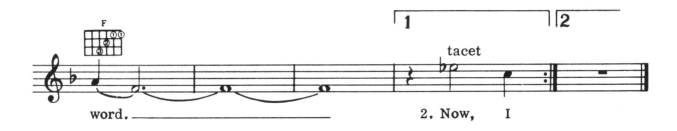

word._____ 2. Now, I

I Got Stung

Words and music by Aaron Schroeder and David Hill

Bright Rock tempo

Ho - ly smoke — a - land sakes a - live! — I nev - er

thought this could hap-pen to me. _____ Mm, _____

Yeah! Mm, _____ Yeah! I got stung by a sweet hon-ey
she had all that I want-ed and

bee. Oh, what a feel - ing come o - ver me. It
more. And I've seen hon-ey bees be - fore. Start - ed

start - ed in my eyes, crept up to my__ head, F -
buzz - in' in my ear, buzz - in' in my brain, Got

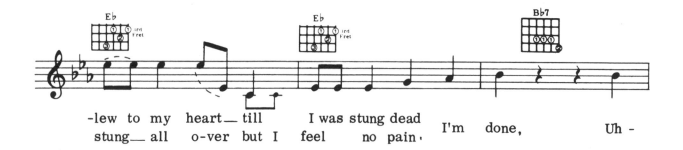

-lew to my heart— till I was stung dead
stung— all o-ver but I feel no pain· I'm done, Uh -

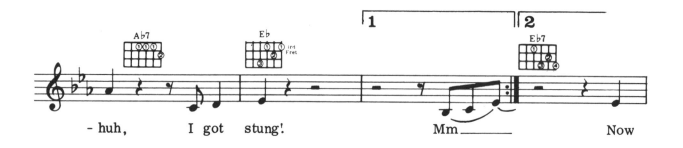

- huh, I got stung! Mm_____ Now

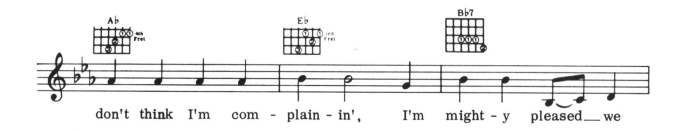

don't think I'm com - plain - in', I'm might - y pleased— we

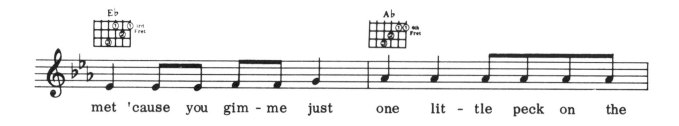

met 'cause you gim - me just one lit - tle peck on the

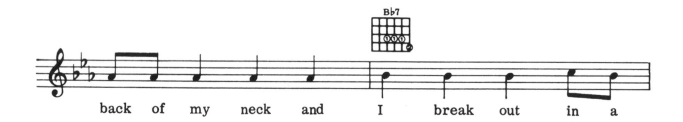

back of my neck and I break out in a

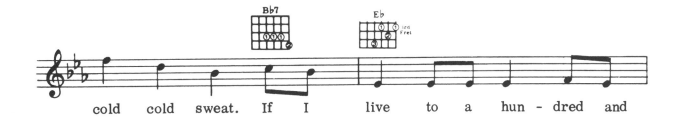

cold cold sweat. If I live to a hun - dred and

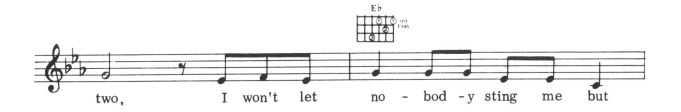

two, I won't let no - bod -y sting me but

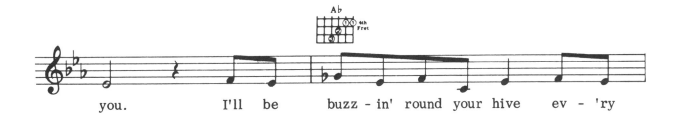

you. I'll be buzz - in' round your hive ev - 'ry

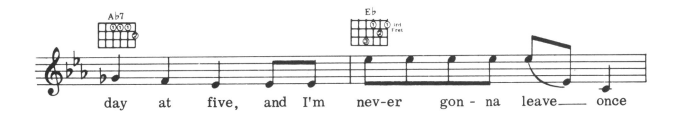

day at five, and I'm nev-er gon - na leave___ once

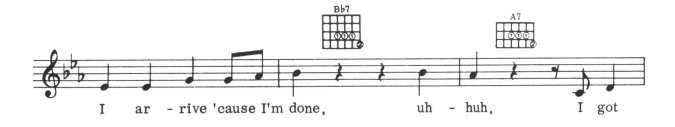

I ar - rive 'cause I'm done, uh - huh, I got

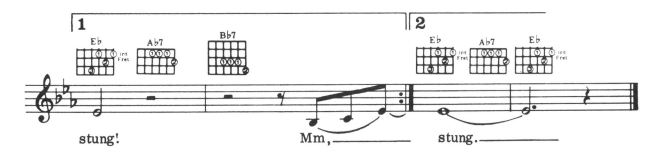

stung! Mm,_____ stung._____

You're The Devil In Disguise

Words and music by Bill Giant, Bernie Baum and Florence Kaye

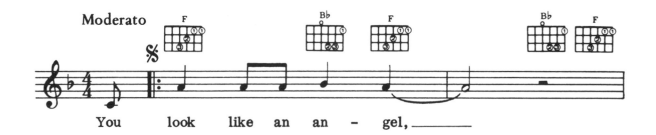

You look like an an - gel, _____

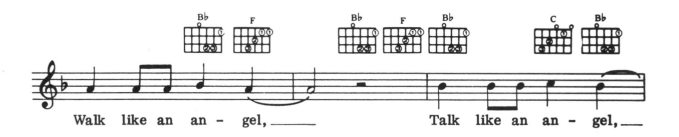

Walk like an an - gel, _____ Talk like an an - gel, ___

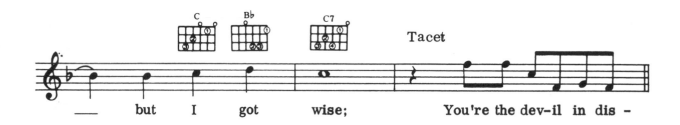

___ but I got wise; You're the dev-il in dis -

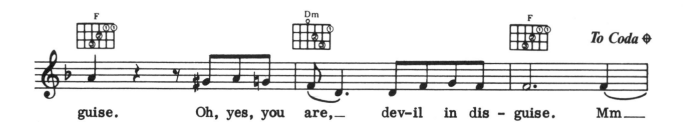

guise. Oh, yes, you are,___ dev-il in dis - guise. Mm___

1. You fooled me— with your kiss - es,
2. I thought that— I was in heav - en,

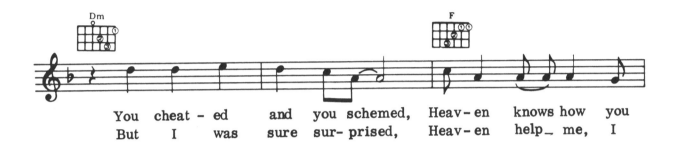

You cheat - ed and you schemed, Heav-en knows how you
But I was sure sur- prised, Heav-en help— me, I

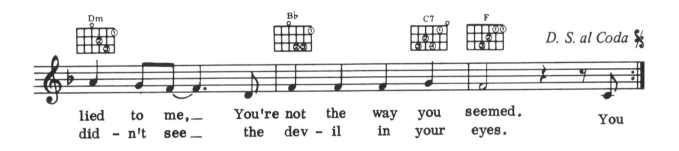

D. S. al Coda 𝄋

lied to me,— You're not the way you seemed. You
did - n't see— the dev - il in your eyes.

⊕ *CODA*

Repeat ad lib. fading-out

— Dev-il in dis - guise, Oh, yes, you are. Dev-il in dis -

No More Heroes

Words and music by The Stranglers

In The Shadows
Words and music by The Stranglers

Across The Universe

Words and music by John Lennon and Paul McCartney

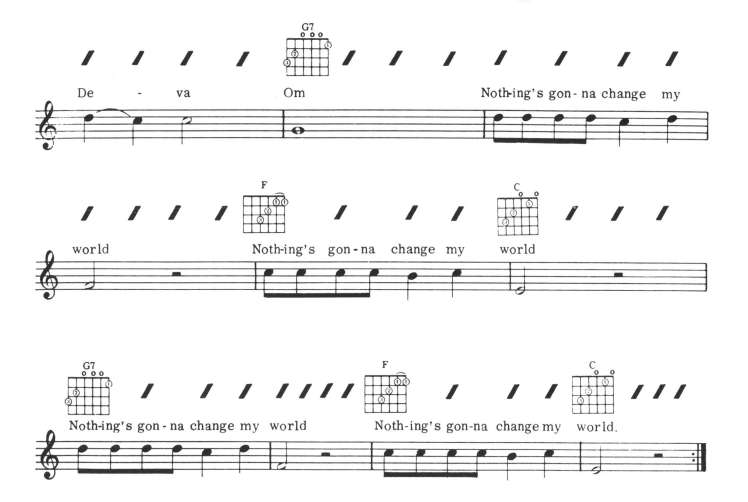

De - va   Om   Noth-ing's gon - na change   my

world   Noth-ing's gon - na change my   world

Noth-ing's gon - na change my world   Noth-ing's gon-na change my   world.

Images of broken light
Which dance **before** me like a million eyes,
That call me on and on
Across the universe

Thoughts meander like a restless wind inside a letter box
They tumble blindly as they **make their way**
Across the universe

Sounds of laughter shades of earth
Are ringing through my open views
Inciting and inviting me.

Limitless undying love
Which shines around me like a million suns
It calls me on and on
Across the universe.

Jai __ Gu - ru __ De - va.

Keep repeating till fade

Come Together

Words and music by John Lennon and Paul McCartney

toe   jam foot-ball, He got   mon - key fin - ger, He shoot   co - ca co - la, He say,
wal - rus gum-boot, He got   O - no side-board,He one   spi - nal crack-er, He got
ear - ly warn-ing He got   Mud - dy Wa-ter,He one   Mo - jo fil - ter, He say,

A7

"I know_____ you,   you   know   me."
feet _____ down   be - low   his   knee
"One and_____ one   and   one   is   three."

G7

One thing I   can   tell you   is   you   got   to   be   free
Hold you   in   his   arm - chair,you can   feel his   di - sease.   Come To
Got   to   be   good look - ing 'cause he   so   hard to   see.

Bm   G   D7

geth- er,____   right   now, _____   o - ver me._____

1. 2. 3. *last time fade*

In My Life

Words and music by John Lennon and Paul McCartney

I've Got The Music In Me
Words and music by Bias Boshell

Moderately, with a strong Four Beat

VERSE

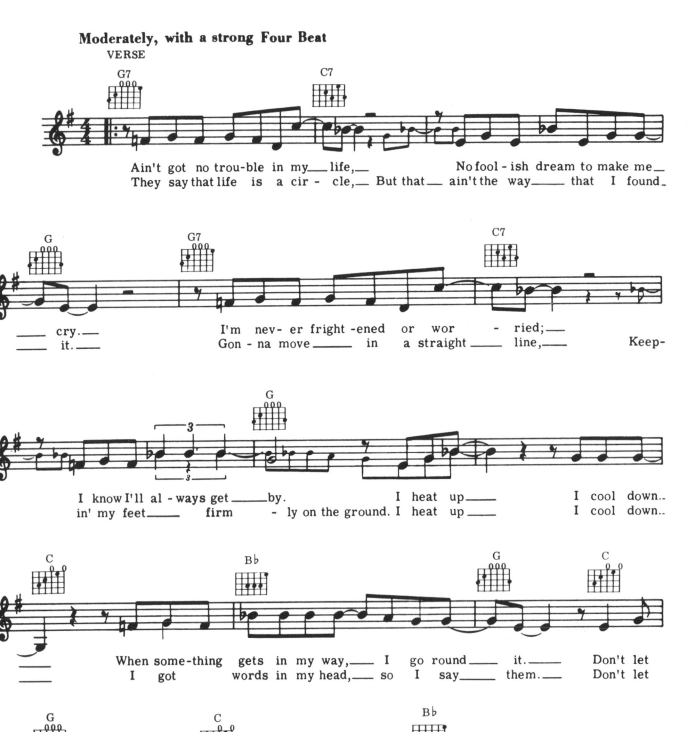

Ain't got no trou-ble in my___ life,___   No fool-ish dream to make me___
They say that life is a cir-cle,___ But that__ ain't the way___ that I found_

___ cry.___   I'm nev-er fright-ened or wor - ried;___
___ it. ___   Gon-na move___ in a straight___ line,___ Keep-

I know I'll al-ways get___by.   I heat up___ I cool down..
in' my feet___ firm - ly on the ground. I heat up___ I cool down..

When some-thing gets in my way,___ I go round___ it.___ Don't let
I got words in my head,___ so I say___ them.___ Don't let

life get me down;___ Gon-na take it___ the way___
life get me down;___ Catch a-hold___ of my blues___ and just play___

CHORUS

_____ that I found___ it.____ }
_____ them.____

I got the mu-sic in___ me,   I got the mu-sic in___ me,

I got the mu-sic in me._____   I got the mu-sic in___ me.

I got the mu-sic in___ me,   I got the mu-sic in me._____

_____   Feel funk - y,___   feel good,_____   Gon - na tell___ you I'm___

_____ in the neigh - bour-hood.___ Gon-na fly___ like a bird_____ on the wing.___ Hold on___

_____ to your hat,___ hon - ey,   sing, sing,___ sing, sing,_____   Heat up;   cool___

_____down;___   I got words_____ in my head,___ so I sing_____them.___   Don't let

D. S. and fade out on Chorus

life___ get me down;_____   Catch a-hold_____of my blues___ and just play_____them.___

101

Lady Madonna

Words and music by John Lennon and Paul McCartney

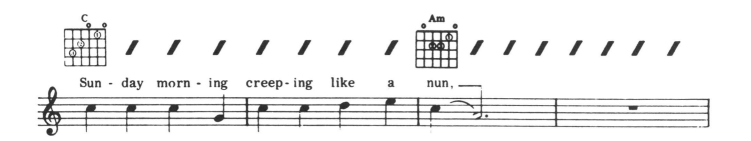

Sun - day morn - ing creep - ing like a nun, ——

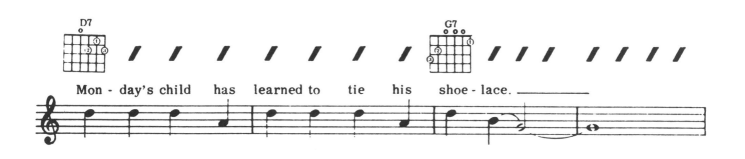

Mon - day's child has learned to tie his shoe - lace. ——

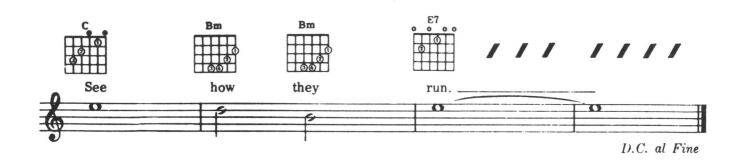

See how they run. ——

D.C. al Fine

Lady Madonna, baby at your breast,
Wonder how you manage to feed the rest.
Lady Madonna lying on the bed,
Listen to the music playing in your head.

Tuesday afternoon is never ending,
Wednesday morning papers didn't come,
Thursday night your stocking needed mending,
See how they run.

Sgt. Pepper's Lonely Hearts Club Band

Words and music by John Lennon and Paul McCartney

Moderately Bright

CHORUS

We're Ser-geant Pep-per's Lone - ly Hearts Club Band We hope you will en-joy the show.

We're Ser-geant Pep-per's Lone - ly Hearts Club Band. Sit back and let the eve-ning go, Ser-geant Pep-per's Lone - ly, Ser-geant Pep-per's Lone - ly, Ser-geant Pep-per's Lone - ly - Heart's Club Band.

Lucy In The Sky With Diamonds

Words and music by John Lennon and Paul McCartney

Cel - lo - phane flow - ers of yel - low and green tow - er - ing o - ver your head. Look for the girl with the sun in her eyes and she's gone. Lu - cy in the sky___ with dia - monds, Lu - cy in the sky___ with dia - monds, Lu - cy in the sky___ with dia - monds. Ah!

*D.C. for extra verses
last time, D.S. and fade*

Follow her down to a bridge by a fountain
Where rocking horse people eat marshmallow pies.
Ev'ryone smiles as you drift past the flowers
That grow so incredibly high.
Newspaper taxis appear on the shore waiting to take you away
Climb in the back with your head in the clouds and you're gone.

Chorus

Picture yourself on a train in a station
With plasticine porters with looking glass ties.
Suddenly someone is there at the turnstile
The girl with the kaleidoscope eyes.

Chorus

Catch The Wind

Words and music by Donovan

1. In the chill - y _____ hours and min-utes of un -
2. feel you _____ all a - round me and to

cer - tain- ty_____ I want to be _____ in the warm _
take your hand_____ a - long the sand_____ Ah but I

_ hold of your lov - in' mind _____
may as well try and

2. To catch the wind

3. When - sun - down ____ pales the sky I want to
4. me to _____ love you now would be the
5. rain has _____ hung the leaves with tears ____ I
6. Stand-in' _____ in your heart is where I

hide   a   while___   be - hind your   smile___   And ev - 'ry -
sweet - est thing___   't'would make me   sing___   Ah but   I
want   you near___   to   kill my   fears___   To help me
want   to   be___   and long to   be___   Ah but   I

where   I'd   look, your eyes I'd   find___
may   as   well   try   and
to   leave all   my blues be - hind___
may   as   well   try   and

4. For catch the wind.

Did - dy___   di - dee dee did - dy did - dy_____ did - dy

did - dy_____ did - dy did - dy___ dee dee dee.___

D.S. al. Coda

CODA

5. When

109

Something's Happening
Words and music by Peter Frampton

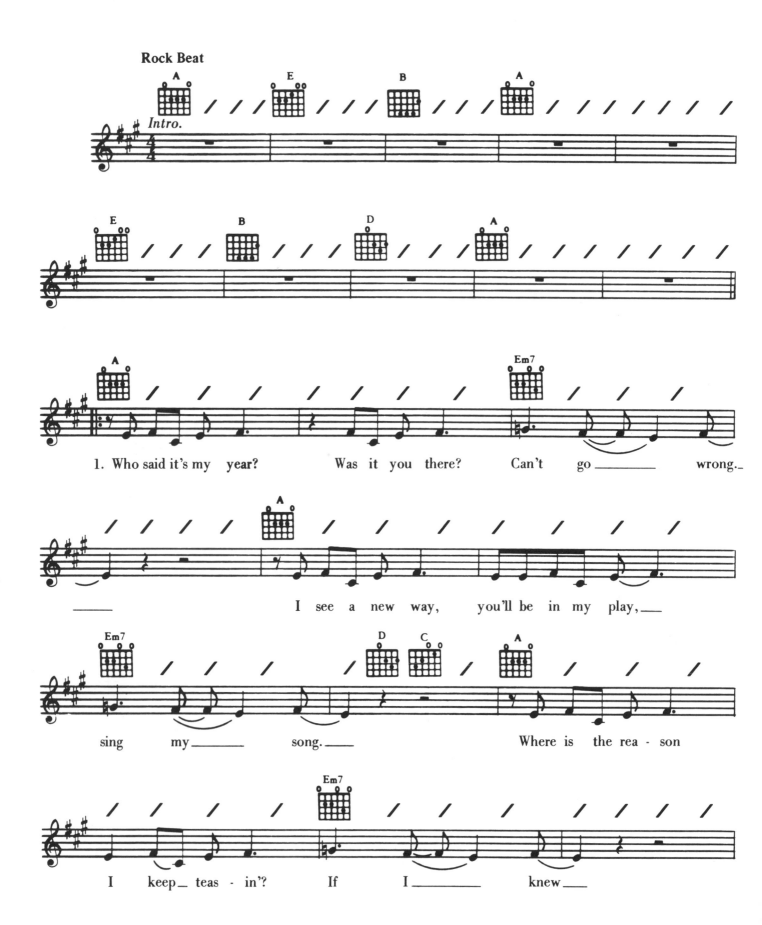

1. Who said it's my year? Was it you there? Can't go ___ wrong. ___

___ I see a new way, you'll be in my play, ___

sing my ___ song. ___ Where is the rea - son

I keep ___ teas - in'? If I ___ knew ___

how to see the new year,   not be - in' blue here

ev - er _____ more. _____

Chorus

All right__   some - thin's hap - p'nin',   hold tight,__   it

might be__ light - nin'.   Turn off the light,__   some - thin's mov - in'.

Can't sleep at night,__   my heart keeps miss - ing a beat.__

Instrumental

Instrumental after 2nd verse

(twice for Guitar Solo)

Bridge

Oo, _____ ba - by, ___ don't

ev - er let it bring you down. _____ Oo, _____ ba -

by, ___ that's not the way I want it to sound. ___ Oo, ___

_____ ba - by, ___ don't ev - er let it bring you down. __

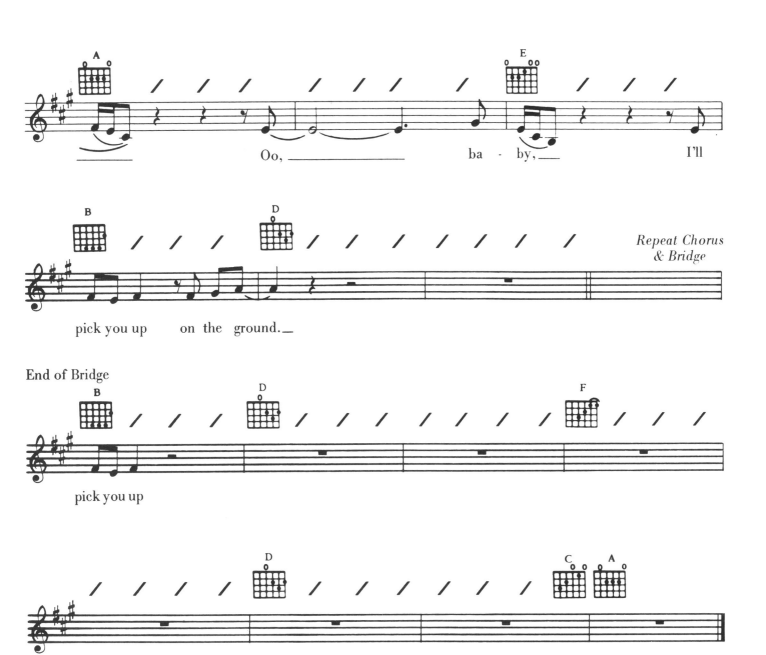

Oo, _____ ba - by, ___ I'll

Repeat Chorus
& Bridge

pick you up on the ground. _

End of Bridge

pick you up

2. I know it's my year, ain't got no fear, hold me down.
   Take it easy, if not for me, sing my song.
   Where is the reason I keep teasin'?
   If I knew how to see the new year, not bein' blue here ever more.

Chorus: All right, somethin's happ'nin', hold tight, it might be lightnin',
   Turn off the light, I feel like dancin'.
   Can't sleep at night, my heart keeps missin' a beat.

Arnold Layne
Words and music by Syd Barrett

1. Arn-old Layne _____ had a strange _
2. On the wall _____ hung a tall _

hob-by _
mir-ror _

collecting clothes.   Moon - shine,
Dis-tort-ed view _   See thru'

1 wash - ing   line _____
   ba - by   blue _____   They suit him   fine. _____

2 _____ He dug it   oh! _ Arn - old Layne.   It's   not   the same.

Takes   two   to know.   Two   to know _   Two to know _

Two to know_(Spoken:) Why can't you see

Instrumental — — — — — — —

to ⊕ Coda

— — Arn-old Layne_____ Arn-old Layne _____ Arn-old Layne _____

_____ Now he's caught _____

_____ a nas-ty sort __ of per-son __ They gave him time

_____ Doors clang chain gang _____ He hates it poor_

D.S. al Coda

____ Arn - old Layne

⊕ **CODA**

____ Arn-old Layne,don't do it a - gain.

Late For The Sky

Words and music by Jackson Browne

Moderately slow

The words had all been spo - ken, and some - how the
me some words come eas - y, but I know that

feel - ing still was - n't right.
they don't mean that ___ much

And still we con -
com - pared with the

tin - ued on ___ through the night,
things that are said when lovers touch.

trac - ing our steps from the be - gin - ning ___ un - til they van - ished in - to the
You nev - er knew what I loved in you, I don't know what you loved in

air, ___
me; ___

try - ing to un - der - stand how our lives had ___ led us
may - be the pic - ture of some - bod - y you were hop - ing I might

there.
be.

Look - ing hard in -
Awake a - gain I

See Emily Play

Words and music by Syd Barrett

The Long And Winding Road

Words and music by John Lennon and Paul McCartney

Yesterday

Words and music by John Lennon and Paul McCartney

Fly Like An Eagle

Words and music by Steve Miller

Moderately, in 2

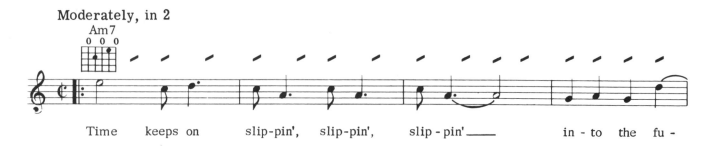

Time keeps on slip-pin', slip-pin', slip-pin' ____ in - to the fu-

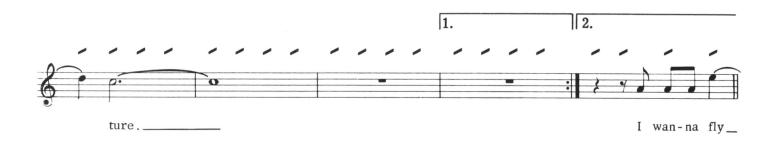

ture. _____

I wan-na fly ____

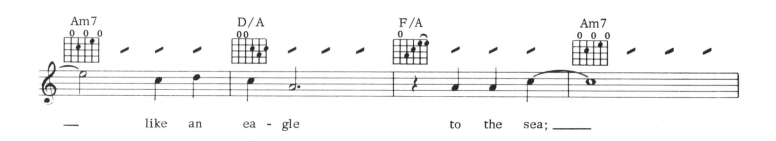

— like an ea - gle to the sea; ____

fly like an ea - gle, let my spir - it car - ry me. I want to

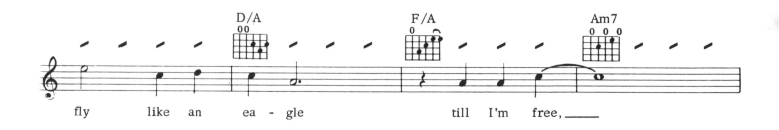

fly like an ea - gle till I'm free, ____

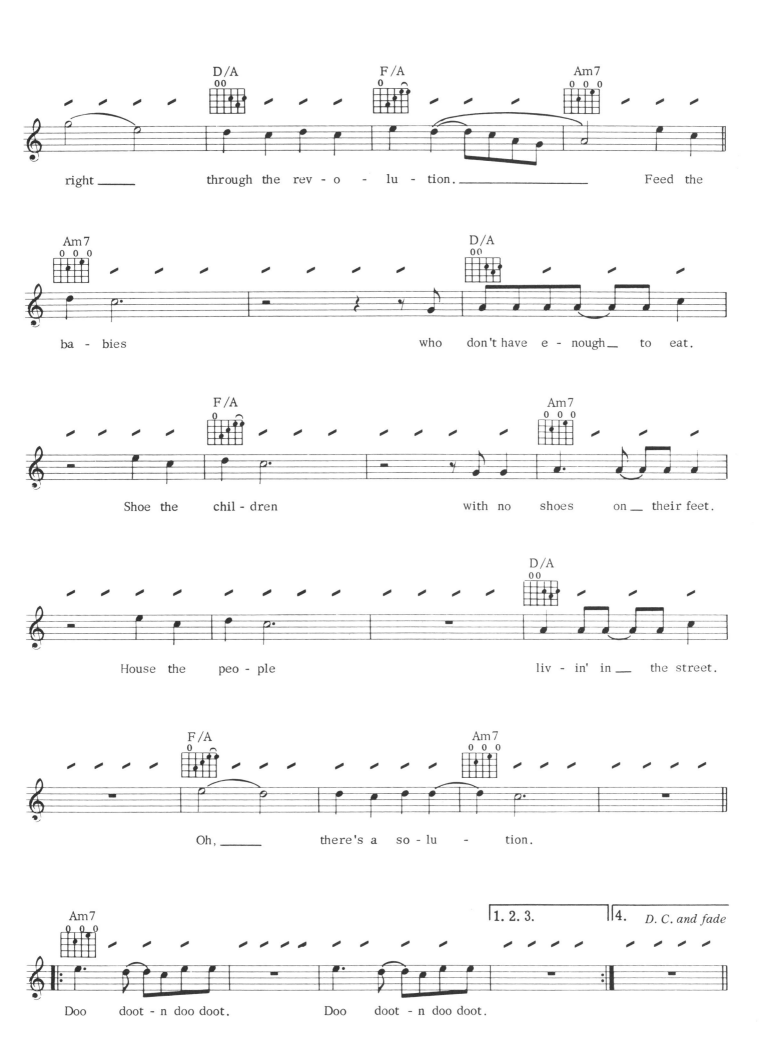

right _____ through the rev - o - lu - tion. _____ Feed the

ba - bies who don't have e - nough _ to eat.

Shoe the chil - dren with no shoes on _ their feet.

House the peo - ple liv - in' in _ the street.

Oh, _____ there's a so - lu - tion.

Doo doot - n doo doot. Doo doot - n doo doot.

1. 2. 3.   4. *D. C. and fade*

The Joker
Words and music by Steve Miller

Slowly, in 2

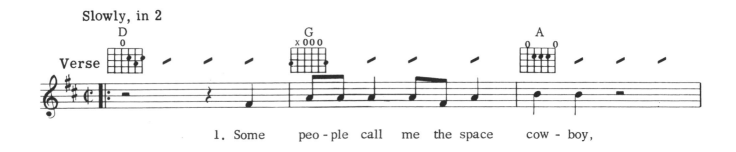

1. Some peo-ple call me the space cow-boy,

yeah.___ Some call me the gang-ster of love.___

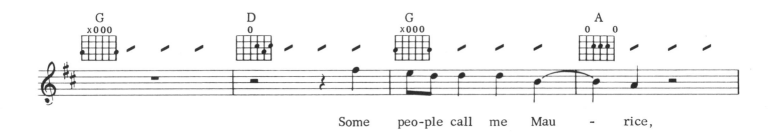

Some peo-ple call me Mau - rice,

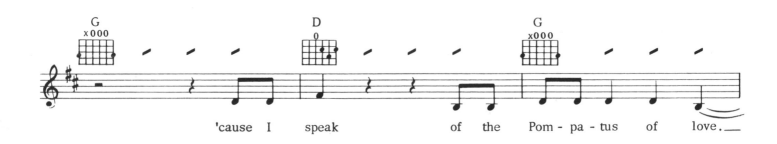

'cause I speak of the Pom - pa - tus of love.___

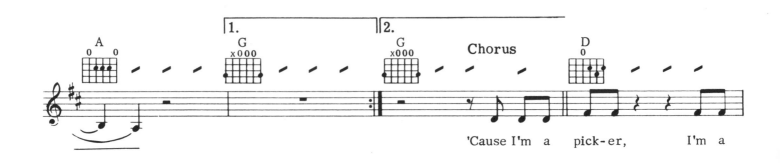

'Cause I'm a pick-er, I'm a

grin-ner, I'm a lov-er and I'm a sin-ner. I play my

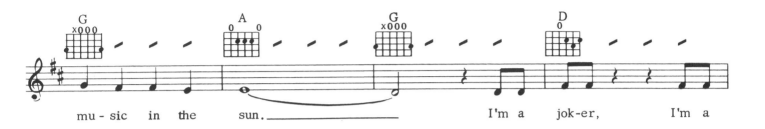

mu - sic in the sun._____ I'm a jok-er, I'm a

smok-er, I'm a mid - night__ tok - er.

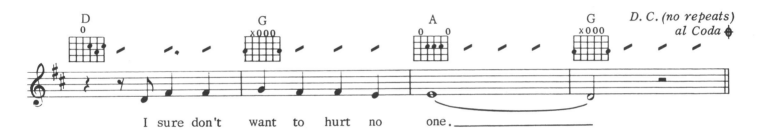

I sure don't want to hurt no one._____

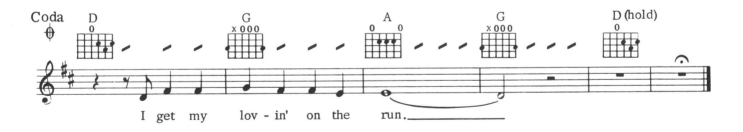

I get my lov - in' on the run._____

2. People talk about me, baby,
   Say I'm doin' you wrong.
   Well, don't you worry, baby,
   'Cause I'm right here at home.

   Chorus

3. You're the cutest thing that I ever did see.
   I really love your peaches, want to shake your tree.
   Lovey-dovey all the time.
   Ooh-ee, baby, I'll sure show you a good time.

   Chorus

Living In The U.S.A.

Words and music by Steve Miller

Moderately fast

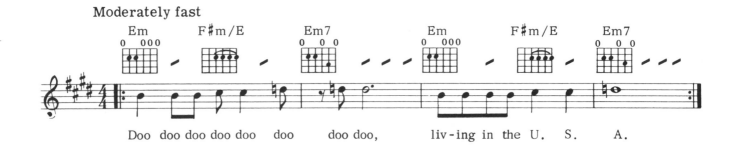

Doo doo doo doo doo doo doo doo, liv-ing in the U. S. A.

Where are you go - ing to?___ What are you gon - na

do?_____ Do you think that it will be eas - y? Do you

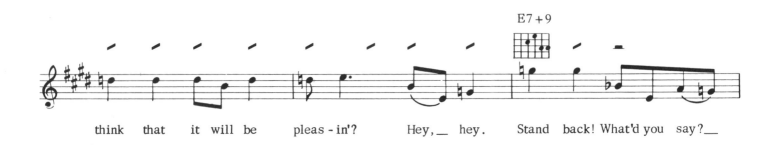

think that it will be pleas - in'? Hey,__ hey. Stand back! What'd you say?__

Stand back! I won't pay.__ Stand back! I'd rath-er play. Stand back! It's my

free-dom. Yeah, don't wor-ry 'bout me, babe. I've

got to be free,_ babe._ Hey, hey, hey,_____ yeah._

Em   F#m/E   Em7   Em   F#m/E   Em7

Doo doo doo doo doo doo doo doo, liv-ing in the U. S. .A.

E7+9   E7+9

Stand back! Di - e - ti - cian! Stand back! Tel - e - vi - sion!

E7+9   E7+9   Em7

Stand back! Pol - i - ti - cian! Stand back! Mor - ti - cian!

Oh, we got to get a - way,_____ a - liv-ing in the U. S. A.

Come on, ba - by. See a

yel-low man, a brown man, white man, a red man

look-ing for Un-cle Sam to give you a help-ing hand. But

ev-'ry-bod-y's kick-ing sand, e-ven pol-i-ti-cians.____ We're

liv-ing in a plas-tic land. Some-bod-y give me a hand, yeah.____

Oh, _____ we're gon-na make it, ba - by._____

Yeah, _____ we've got to shake it, ba - by._____ Yeah,_____ don't

break it, yeah,_ yeah, yeah.

Repeat and fade

Doo doo doo doo doo doo doo doo, liv-ing in the U. S. A.

Rock 'N' Me

Words and music by Steve Miller

Moderate Rock beat

1. Well, I been

look - in' real hard and I'm try'n' to find a job, but it

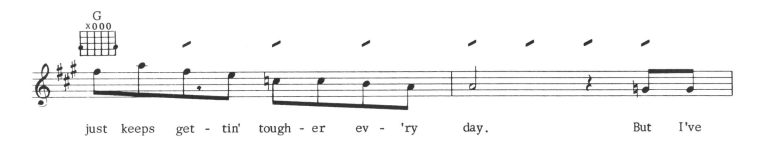

just keeps get - tin' tough - er ev - 'ry day. But I've

got to do my part, 'cause I know in my heart___ I've got to

please my sweet ba - by, yeah.___ 2. Well, I

ain't su - per - sti - tious and I don't get sus - pi - cious, 'cause my

wom - an is a friend of mine. And I

know that it's true that all the things that I do will come

To Coda ⊕

back to me in my sweet time. So keep on

rock - in' me, ba - by. Keep on a - rock - in' me, ba - by.

Keep on a - rock - in' me, ba - by. Keep on a -

1. 2. | 3.

rock - in' me, ba - by. 3. I went from Ba - by, ba - by, ba - by, keep on

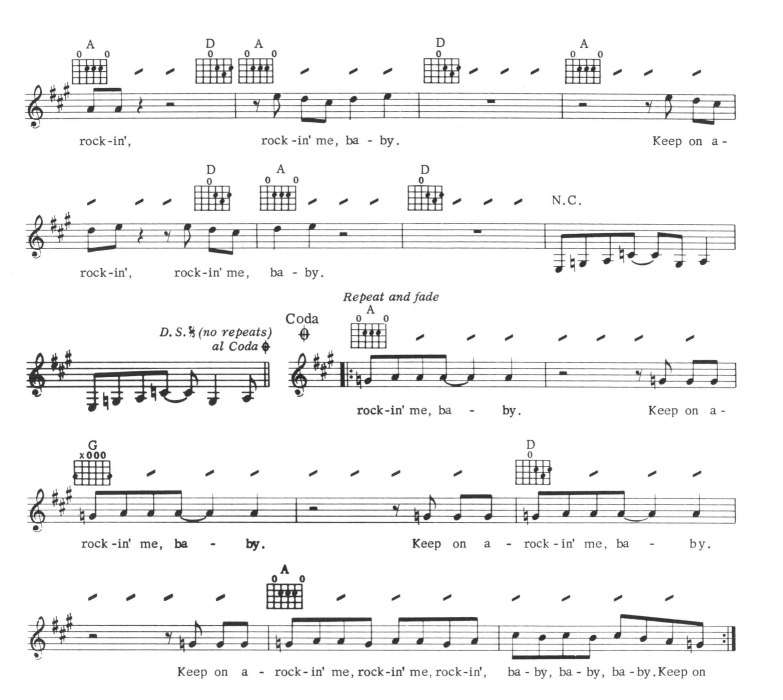

3. I went from Phoenix, Arizona, all the way to Tacoma,
   Philadelphia, Atlanta, L.A.,
   Northern California where the girls are warm
   So I could be with my sweet baby, yeah.
   Keep on a-rockin' me, baby *(etc.)*

4. Don't get suspicious; now don't be suspicious.
   Babe, you know you are a friend of mine.
   And you know that it's true that all the things I do
   Are gonna come back to you in your sweet time.

5. I went from Phoenix, Arizona, all the way to Tacoma,
   Philadelphia, Atlanta, L.A.,
   Northern California where the girls are warm
   So I could hear my sweet baby say:
   Keep on a-rockin' me, baby *(etc.)*

Jungle Love

Words and music by Greg Douglass and Lonnie Turner

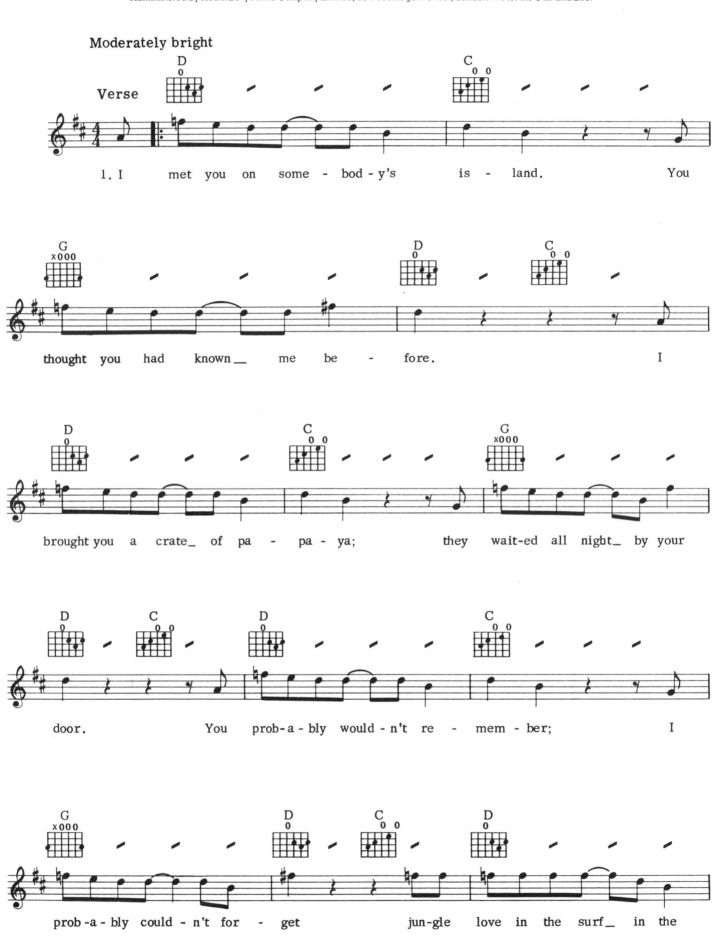

1. I met you on some - bod - y's is - land. You thought you had known __ me be - fore. I brought you a crate __ of pa - pa - ya; they wait - ed all night __ by your door. You prob - a - bly would - n't re - mem - ber; I prob - a - bly could - n't for - get jun - gle love in the surf __ in the

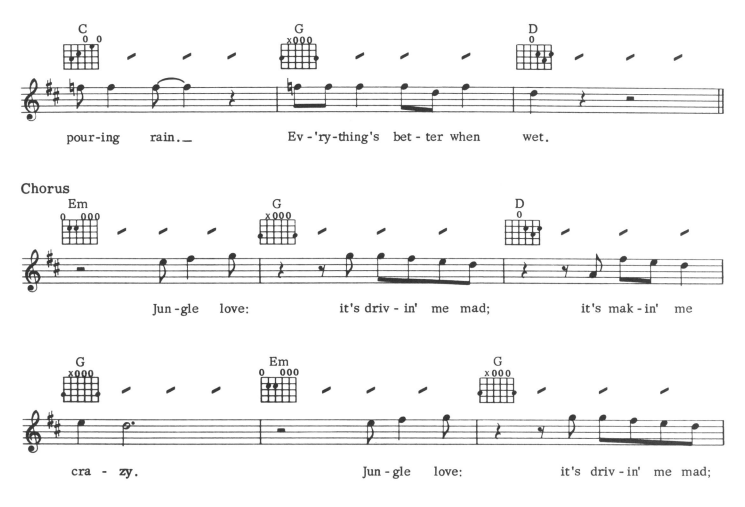

pour-ing   rain.＿   Ev-'ry-thing's bet-ter when   wet.

Chorus

Jun-gle love: it's driv-in' me mad;   it's mak-in' me

cra - zy.   Jun-gle love: it's driv-in' me mad;

it's mak-in' me   cra - zy.   2. But

2. But lately, you live in the jungle. I never see you alone.
   But we need some definite answers, so I thought I would write you a poem.
   The question to everyone's answer is usually asked from within.
   But the patterns of the rain and the truth they contain,
       they have written my life on your skin.

(Chorus)

3. You treat me like I was your ocean: you swim in my blood when it's warm.
   My cycles of circular motion protect you and keep you from harm.
   You live in a world of illusion where everything's peaches and cream.
   We all face a scarlet conclusion, but we spend our time in a dream.

(Chorus)

Space Cowboy

Words and music by Steve Miller and Ben Sidran

Moderate Rock beat

1. I told you 'bout liv-ing in the U. S. of A.___ Don't you know I'm a gang-ster of love? Let me tell you, peo-ple, that I found a new way.___ And I'm tired of all talk a-bout___ love,___ and the same old sto - ry with a new set of words___ a-bout the good and the bad___ and the poor. And the times keep on chang - ing, so I'm keep-ing on top___ of ev - 'ry

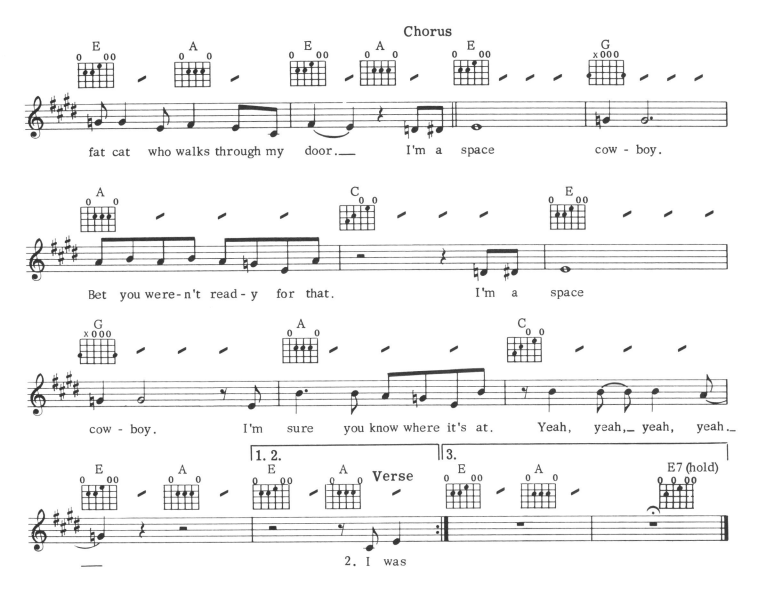

2. I was born on this rock and I've been travelin' through space
   Since the moment I first realized
   What all you fast-talking cats would do if you could.
   You know, I'm ready for the final surprise.
   Ain't no way around it, ain't nothing to say
   That's gonna **satisfy** my soul deep inside.
   All the players and surveyors keep the **whole place** uptight
   While it keeps on getting darker outside.

   (Chorus)

3. I see the showdown, slow downs, **lost and** found, turn arounds,
   The boys in some military shirts.
   I keep some eyes on thighs, on the low and falling skys,
   And I don't let my friends get hurt.
   All you back-room schemers, small-trip dreamers,
   Better find something new to say,
   'Cause you're the same old story; it's the same old crime
   And you got heavy dues to pay.

   (Chorus)

Dancing Queen

Words and music by Benny Andersson, Stig Anderson and Bjorn Ulvaeus

watch that_ scene_ dig-gin' the dan - cing_ queen._____

Fri - day night_and the lights are low,___

__ look-ing out_for a place to go,_____ Mm____

where they play_the right mu-sic, get - ting in_the swing, you come to look for a king.

__ An - y - bod - y could see that guy_
You're a tea - ser you turn them on____

___ night is young_and the mu-sic's high_____
___ leave 'em burn-ing and then you're gone____

139

With a bit of rock mu - sic ev -'ry - thing is fine)
look-ing out for an - oth - er an - y - one will do) You're in the

mood for a dance   and when you get the chance

You are the danc - ing queen

young and sweet, on - ly sev - en - teen

danc - ing queen, feel the beat from the tam - bour - ine Oh

yeh,   You can dance, you can jive,

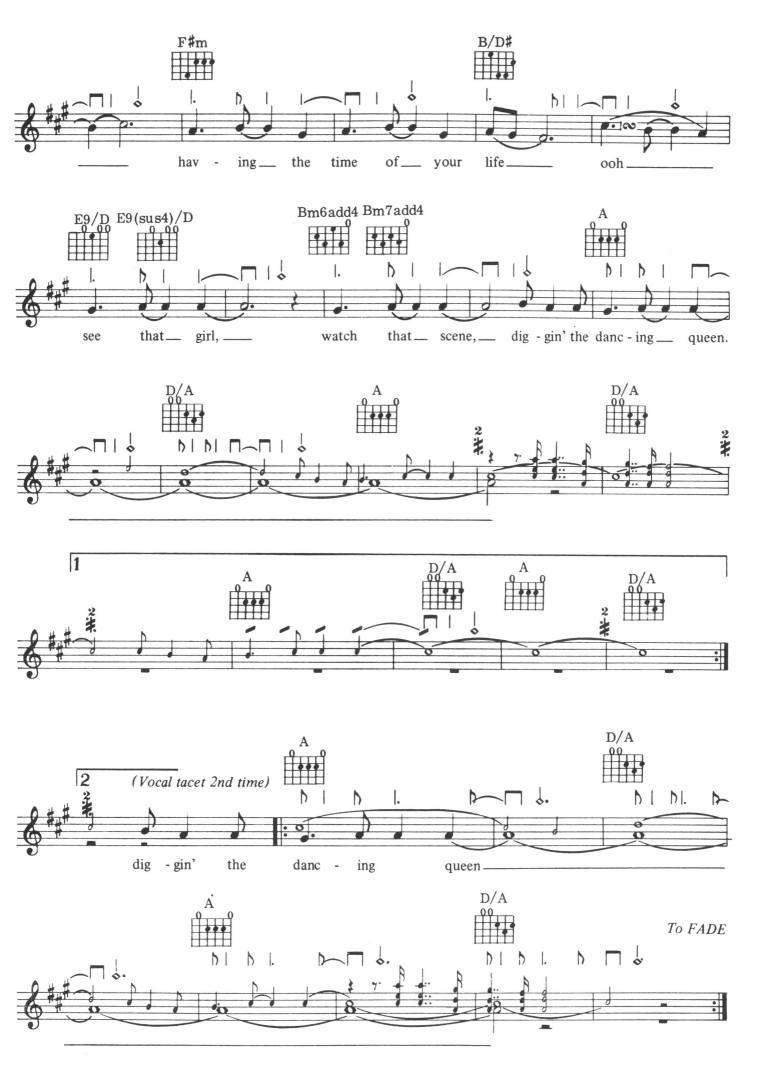

Photographs And Memories

Words and music by Jim Croce

Love Machine

Words and music by D. Byron, K. Hensley and M. Box

Love-ly lit - tle la - dy, you've got me on the
Said she was a los-er, the kind that came off
On - ly time she's hap-py, is when the bul - lets

run.
worst.
fly.

You're a love mach-ine___ and you
So I had to try___ hard
And she'll make you feel you're better than

say that I'm your gun.
to sat - isfy your thirst.
an - y oth - er guy.

But
But
But

I don't care___ 'cos I've got to know. _____

[Instr. _____]

2. She
3. The

The Wizard

Words and music by K. Hensley and M. Clark

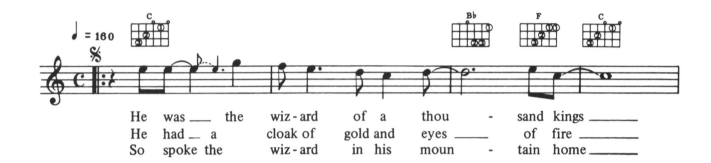

He was ___ the wiz-ard of a thou - sand kings _____
He had ___ a cloak of gold and eyes _____ of fire _____
So spoke the wiz-ard in his moun - tain home _____

And I chanced to meet ___ him one ___ night wan - der - ing ___
And as he spoke ___ I felt ___ a deep de - sire ___
The vis - ion of his wis - dom means we'll nev - er be a - lone

_____ He told me tales _____ and he drank ___ my
_____ To free the world _____ of its fear _____ and
_____ And I will dream _____ of my mag - ic

wine Me and ___ my mag - ic man ___ kind - a
pain And help ___ the peo - ple ple to _____ feel
night And the mil - lion sil - ver stars ___ that

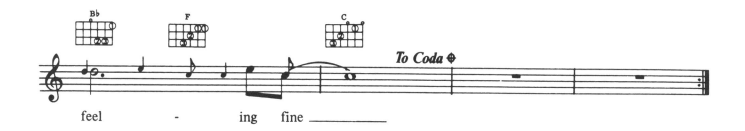

feel - ing fine _____

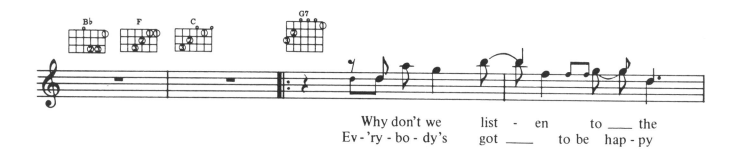

Why don't we list - en to ___ the
Ev - 'ry - bo - dy's got ___ to be hap - py

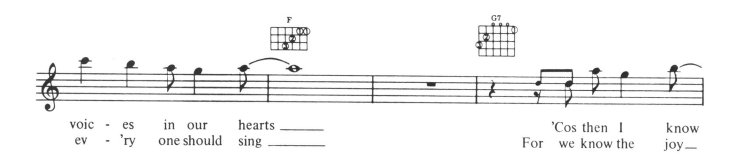

voic - es in our hearts _____
ev - 'ry one should sing _____

'Cos then I know
For we know the joy—

___ we'd find ___ we're not so far a - part _____
___ of life ___ that peace and love can bring _____

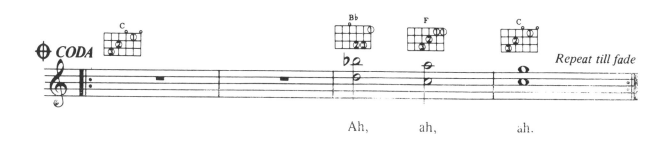

Ah, ah, ah.

Ring Of Fire

Words and music by Merle Kilgore and June Carter

1. Love   is a burn - ing   thing   and it
    taste   of   love is   sweet   when

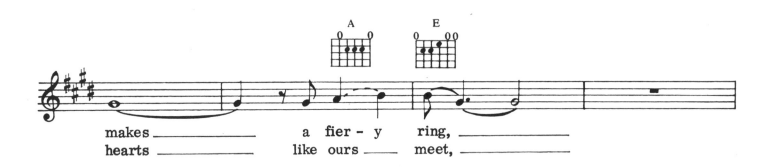

makes _____ a fier - y   ring, _____
hearts _____ like ours ____ meet, _____

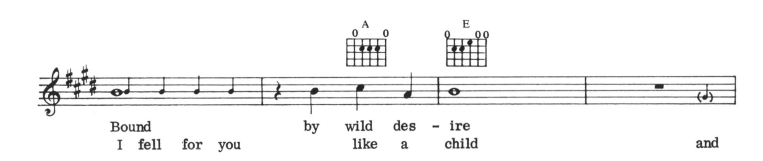

Bound   by   wild des - ire
I fell for you   like   a   child   and

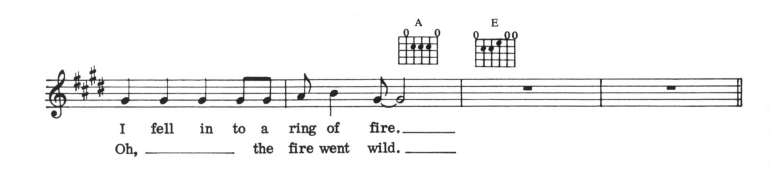

I   fell   in   to   a   ring of   fire. _____
Oh, _____ the fire went   wild. _____

I fell in - to a burn - ing ring of

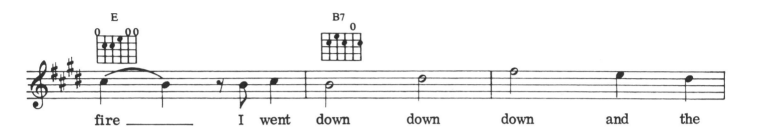

fire _____ I went down down down and the

flame went high - er and it burns burns burns.

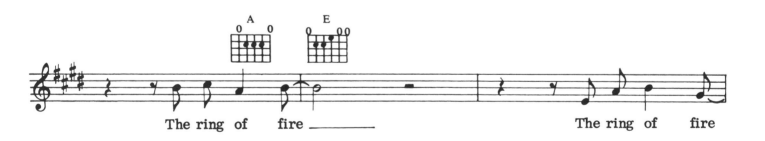

The ring of fire _____ The ring of fire

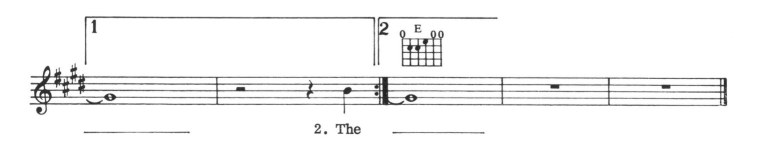

_____ 2. The _____

Bike
Words and music by Syd Barrett

Four times

1. I've got a bike, you can ride it if you like it's got a

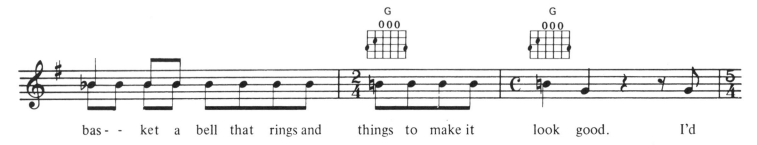

bas - - ket a bell that rings and things to make it look good. I'd

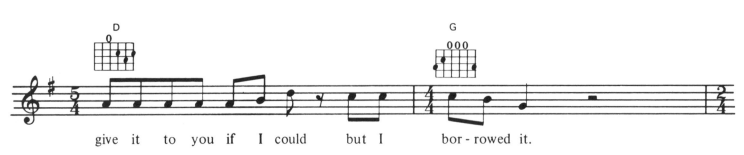

give it to you if I could but I bor - rowed it.

(Spoken:) You're the kind of girl that fits in with my world. I'll give you

an - y - thing and ev' - ry - thing if you want things.

Last time – Slower

I know a room of mus-i-cal tunes so write some chief, most of them have

got one. Let's go in-to the oth-er room and make them work.

2. I've got a cloak, it's a bit of a joke.
   There's a tear up the front, it's red and black
   I've had it for months.
   If you think it could look good, then I guess it should.
   (spoken) You're the kind of girl that fits in with my world.
   I'll give you anything and everything if you want things.

3. I know a mouse and he hasn't got a house
   I don't know why I call him Gerald.
   He's getting rather old but he's a good mouse.
   You're the kind of girl that fits in with my world.
   I'll give you anything and everything if you want things.

4. I've got a clan of ginger-bread men –
   Here a man, there a man, lot's of ginger-bread men
   Take a couple if you wish - they're on the dish.
   You're the kind of girl that fits in with my world.
   I'll give you anything and everything if you want things.

Last Time

I know a room of musical tunes.
So write some chief
Most of them have got one
Let's go into the other room -
and make them work.

For Everyman
Words and music by Jackson Browne

Moderately

1. Ev-'ry-bod-y I talk to is read-y to leave with the light of the morn-ing. They've seen the end com-ing down long e-nough_ to be-lieve that they've heard their last warn-ing. Stand-ing a-lone, each has his own tick-et in his hand. And as the eve-ning de-scends I sit think-ing 'bout Ev-'ry-man.

Wait-ing here for Ev-'ry-man,____ make it on your own_ if you think you can. If you see_ some-where to go,____ I un-der-stand.____

Wait-ing here for Ev-'ry-man,____ don't ask me if he'll show,

ba-by, I don't know. _____ Make it on your own_ if you think you can;_____ some-where lat-er on you'll have to take a stand,_ then you're gon-na need a hand._____ I'm not try'ng to tell you that I've seen the plan; turn and walk a-way_ if you think I am._ But don't think too bad-ly of one who's left hold-ing sand;_ he's just an-oth-er dream-er dream-ing 'bout Ev-'ry-man.

2. Seems like I've always been looking for some other place
   To get it together,
   Where with a few of my friends I could give up the race
   And maybe find something better.
   But all my fine dreams,
   Well thought out schemes to gain the motherland
   Have all eventually come down to waiting for Everyman.

   Waiting here for Everyman, *(etc.)*

3. Everybody's just waiting to hear from the one
   Who can give them the answers
   And lead them back to that place in the warmth of the sun
   Where sweet childhood still dances.
   Who'll come along
   And hold out that strong but gentle father's hand?
   Long ago I heard someone say something 'bout Everyman.

   Waiting here for Everyman, *(etc.)*

House Of The Rising Sun

Words and music by Alan Price

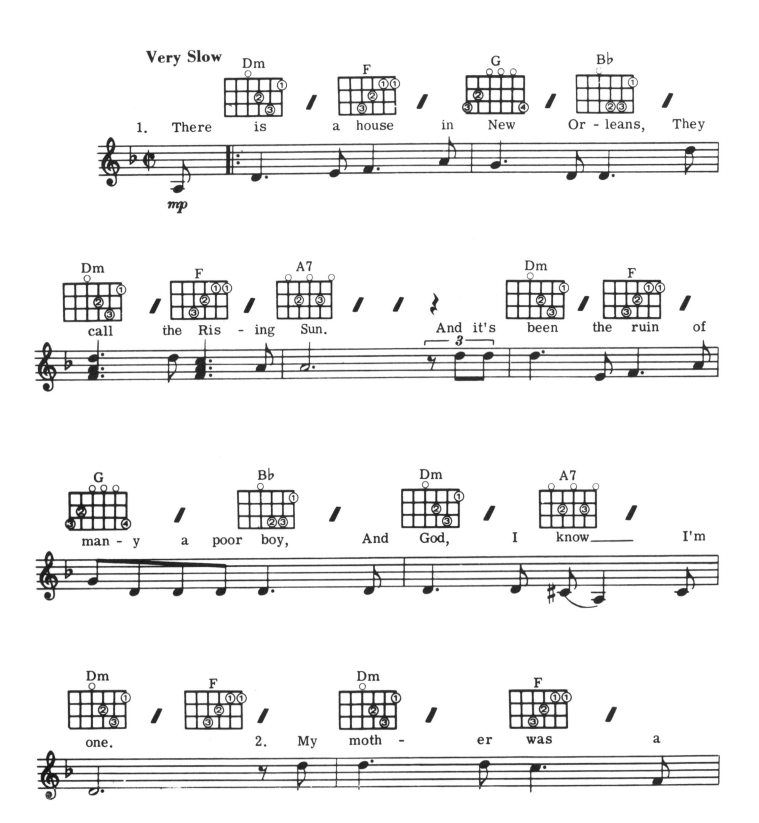

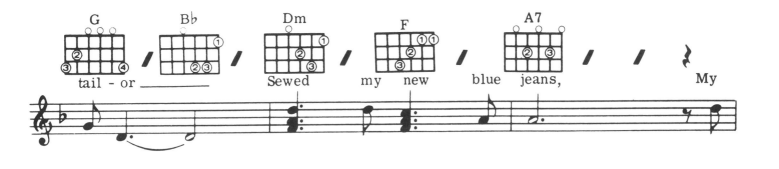

tail - or _____ Sewed my new blue jeans, My

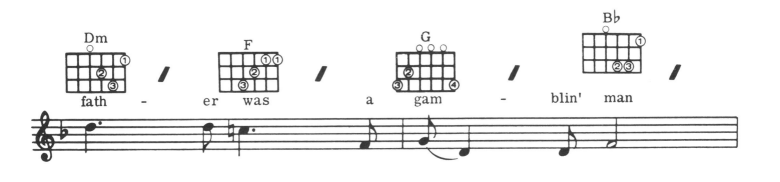

fath - er was a gam - blin' man

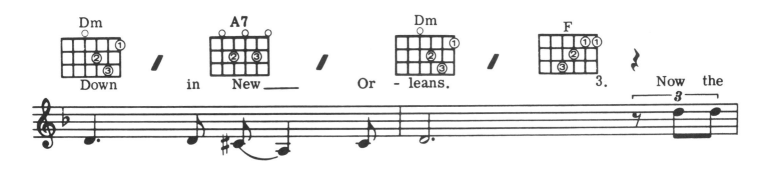

Down in New _____ Or - leans. 3. Now the

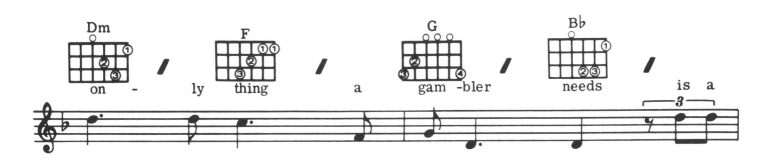

on - ly thing a gam -bler needs is a

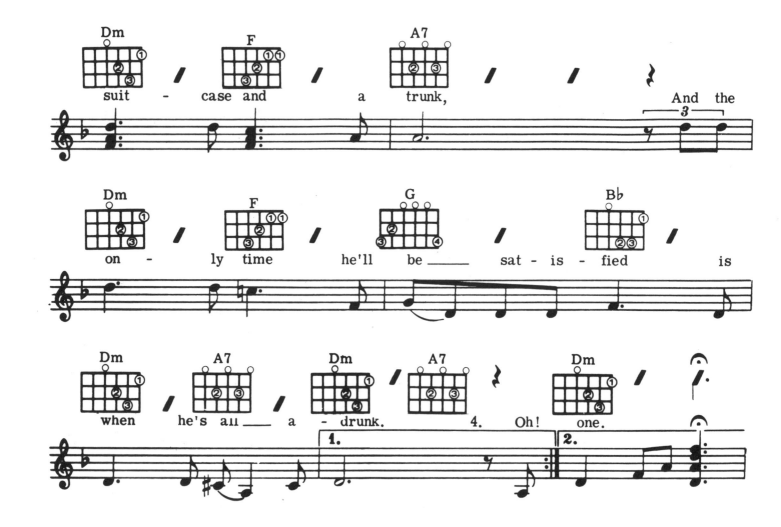

4. Oh! mother, tell your children
   Not to do what I have done.
   Spend your lives in sin and misery
   In The House Of The Rising Sun.

5. Well, I've got one foot on the platform,
   The other foot on the train.
   I'm going back to New Orleans
   To wear that ball and chain.

6. Well, there is a house in New Orleans,
   They call the Rising Sun,
   And it's been the ruin of many a poor boy,
   And God, I know, I'm one.

Livin' Thing

Words and music by Jeff Lynne

1. Sail - in' a - way___ on the crest___ of a wave,___ it's like
2. Mak - in' be - lieve___ this is what___ you con - ceived___ from your
3. Tak - in' a dive___ 'cause you can't___ halt the slide___ float - ing

mag - ic.   Oh,
worst _____ day.   Oh,
down - stream.   Oh,

roll - in' and rid - in' and slip - pin' and slid - in', it's
mov - ing in line,___ then you look___ back in time ___ to the
so let her go, ___ don't start spoil - ing the show___ it's a

en thing,   What a ter - ri - ble   thing to ____

lose.

lose.   It's a Liv - in' Thing!   It's a ter-
               - en thing.   What a ter-

ri - ble   thing   to ____ lose.   It's a giv -
ri - ble   thing   to ____ lose.   It's a Liv-

157

Something

Words and music by George Harrison

CHORDS USED IN THIS SONG

SUGGESTED STRUM

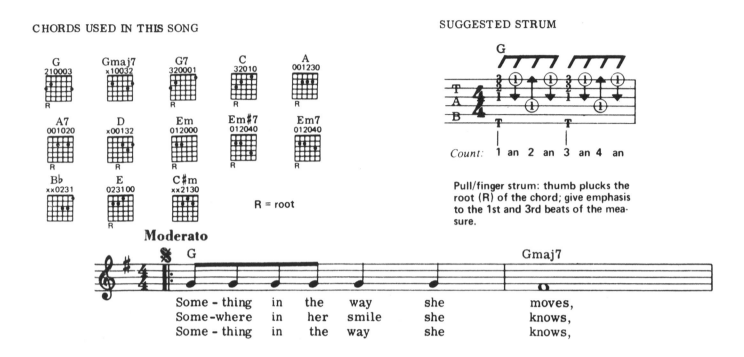

Count: 1 an 2 an 3 an 4 an

Pull/finger strum: thumb plucks the root (R) of the chord; give emphasis to the 1st and 3rd beats of the measure.

R = root

Moderato

G ... **Gmaj7**

Some - thing in the way she moves,
Some-where in her smile she knows,
Some - thing in the way she knows,

G7 ... **C** ... **A** ... **A7**

at-tracts me like no oth - er lov - er; Some-thing in the way she
that I don't need no oth - er lov - er; Some-thing in her style that
and all I have to do is think of her; Some-thing in the things she

D ... **Em** ... **Em#7**

woos me.
shows me.
shows me.
I don't want to leave___ her now. you

Em7 ... **A7** **C** ... **Bb** **D** ... **E** *To Coda*

know I be - lieve___ and how.___

158

You're ask - ing me, will my love grow?

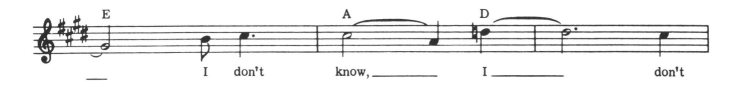
I don't know, I don't

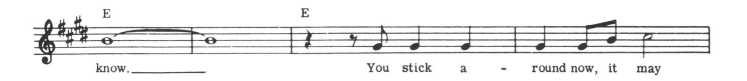
know. You stick a - round now, it may

show; I don't know, I

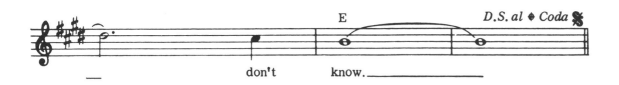
don't know.

159

Well All Right

Words and music by Jerry Allison, Buddy Holly,
Joe Maudlin and Norman Petty

Moderato, with a strong beat

VERSE

Well all right — so I'm — be-ing fool-ish, Well all right
(Well all right) — so I'm — go-in' stead-y, It's all right

— let peo-ple know — A - bout the dreams and wish-es you
— when peo-ple say, — That those — fool-ish kids can't be read-

— wish in the night — when lights — are low. —
- y for the love — that comes — their way. —

CHORUS

Well all right,

Well all right, — Oh, we'll — live and love with all our might, Well all right,

1. Well all right, — Our — life - time love — will be all right, — Well all right, (To Verse)

2. be all right. —

Hotel California

Words and music by Don Henley, Glenn Frey and Don Felder

162

Dm

An - y time of year (an - y time of year), you can
What a nice sur - prise (what a nice sur - prise); bring your

1. **E**

find it here."

2. **E (hold)**

al - i - bis."

Am

Mir - rors on the ceil - ing,
Last thing I re - mem - ber, I was

E

the pink cham - pagne on ice, and she said,
run - ning for the door. I had to find the

G

"We are all just
I had to find the

D

pris - on - ers here of our own de - vice."
pas - sage back to the place I was be - fore.

F

And in the mas - ter's cham - bers,
"Re - lax," said the night man. "We are

C

they gath - ered for the
pro - gramed to re -

Dm

feast. They stab it with their steel - y knives, but they
ceive. You can check out an - y time you like, but

E

1.

just can't kill the beast.
you can nev - er

2. *D. S. % (instrumental) and fade*

leave."

163

Year Of The Cat

Words and music by Al Stewart and Peter Wood

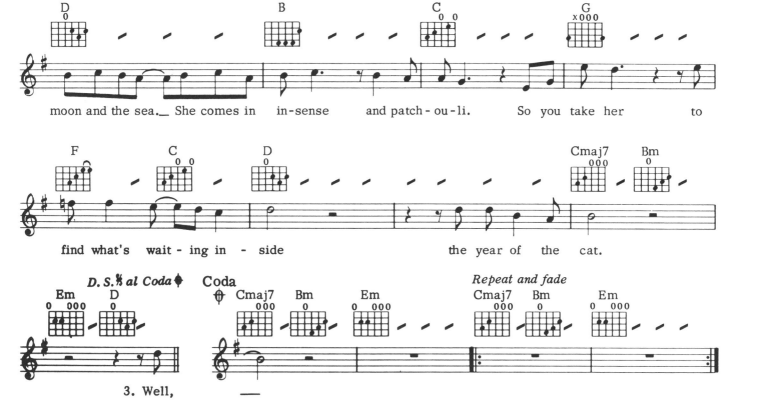

moon and the sea.__ She comes in in-sense and patch-ou-li.   So you take her   to

find what's wait-ing in-side   the year of the cat.

D. S. %al Coda ◆   Coda   *Repeat and fade*

3. Well,   __

Additional lyrics

2. She doesn't give you time for questions
   As she locks up your arm in hers.
   And you follow till your sense of which direction
   Completely disappears.
   By the blue-tiled walls near the market stalls,
   There's a hidden door she leads you to.
   "These days," she says, "I feel my life just like a
   River running through the year of the cat."

3. Well, morning comes and you're still with her
   And the bus and the tourists are gone.
   And you've thrown away your choice and
   Lost your ticket so you have to stay on.
   But the drum-beat strains of the night remain
   In the rhythm of the new-born day.
   You know sometime you're bound to leave her,
   But for now you're gonna stay in the year of the cat.

Peaceful Easy Feeling

Words and music by Jack Tempchin

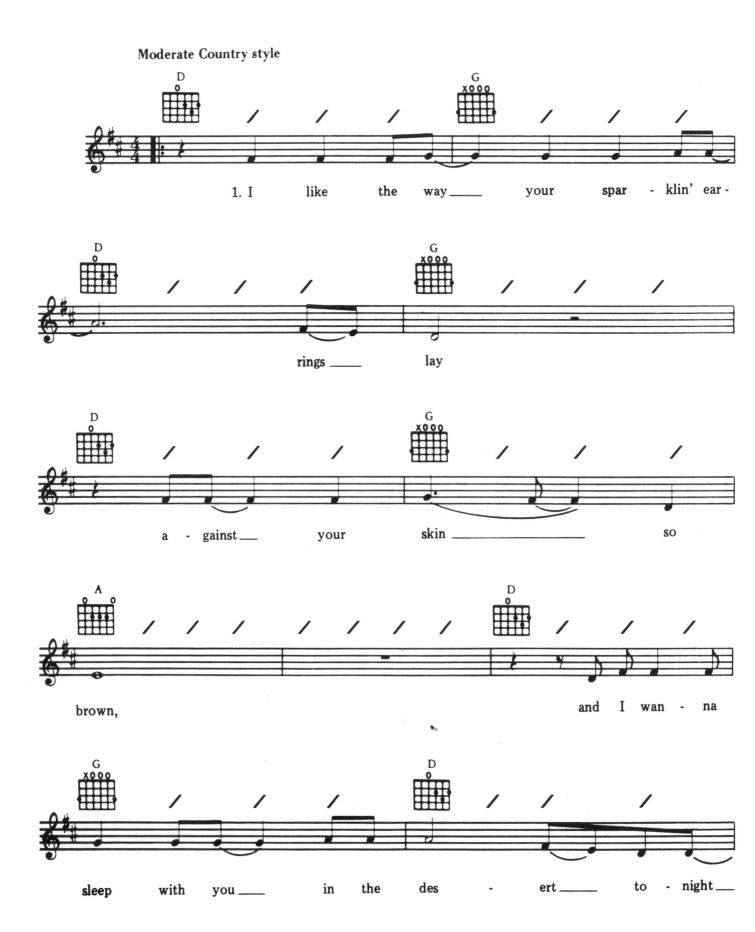

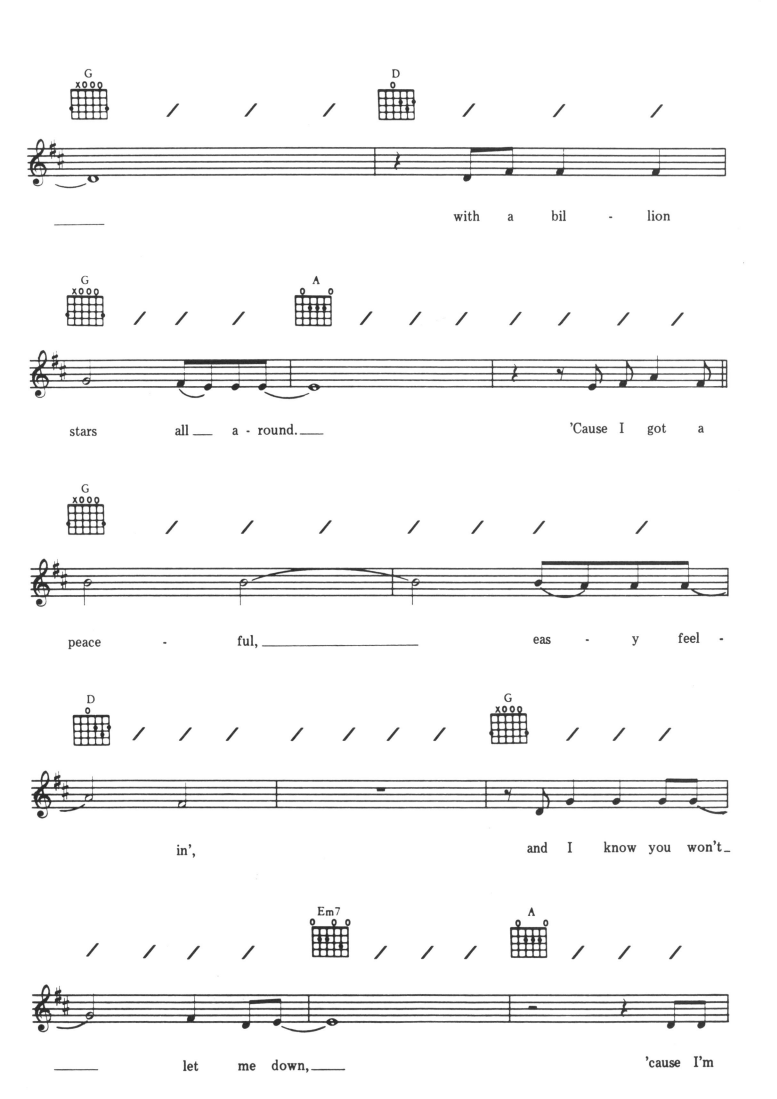

with a bil - lion

stars all a - round. 'Cause I got a

peace - ful, eas - y feel -

in', and I know you won't

let me down, 'cause I'm

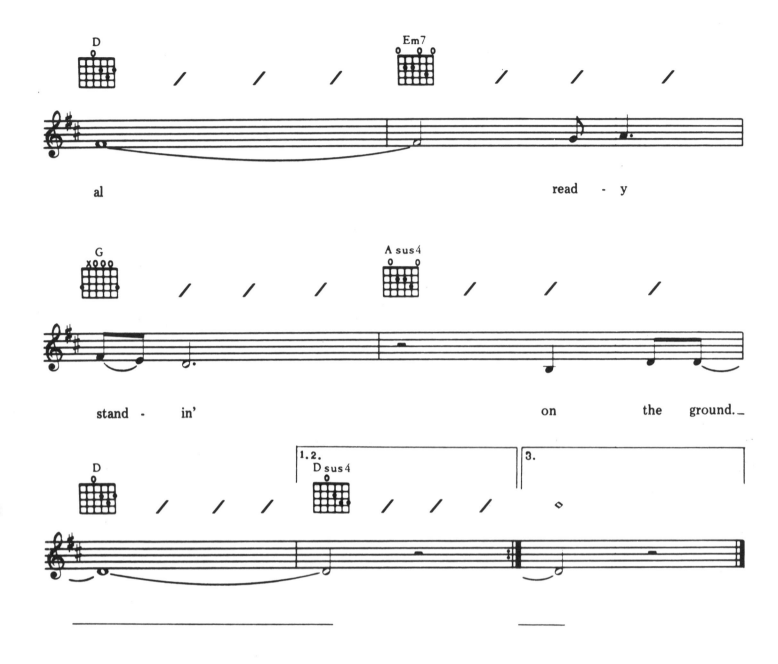

al   read - y

stand - in'   on   the   ground. _

2. And I found out a long time ago
   What a woman can do to your soul;
   Ah, but she can't take you anyway,
   You don't already know how to go.
   And I got a peaceful, easy feelin', (etc.)

3. I get the feelin' I may know you
   As a lover and a friend;
   But this voice keeps whisperin' in my other ear,
   Tells me I may never see you again.
   'Cause I got a peaceful, easy feelin', (etc.)

The Best Of My Love

Words and music by Don Henley, Glenn Frey and John David Souther

Moderately slow

Ev - er - y night ___ I'm ly - in' in bed, ___
Beau - ti - ful fac - es and loud emp - ty plac - es,

hold - in' you close ___ in my dreams, ___ think - in' a - bout ___ all the
look at the way ___ that we live; ___ wast - in' our time ___ on

things that we said and com - in' a - part ___ at the seams.
cheap talk and wine left us so lit - tle to give.

We try to talk it o - ver but the words come out too ___
That same old crowd was like a cold dark cloud that we could never rise a -

rough; I know you were try - in' to give me the best ___ of your ___
bove; but here in my heart ___ I give you the best ___ of my ___

love.
love.

Oh, _____

169

ev - er - y morn - in' I wake up and wor - ry

what's gon - na hap - pen to - day; ____ you see it your __ way and

I see it mine, ____ but we both see it slip - pin' a

way. _____ You know we al - ways had each oth - er, ba - by,

I guess that was - n't e - nough; _____

oh, _____ but here in my heart ___ I

give you the best ___ of my ___ love.

Can't Keep It In

Words and music by Cat Stevens

Oh, I can't keep it in, I can't keep it in, I've got-ta let it out.

I've got __ to show the world, world's __ got-ta see, see all the love,

love that's in me. I said, why walk a - lone, Why wor-ry when it's

warm o-ver here. You've got so much to say, say __ what you mean, mean __

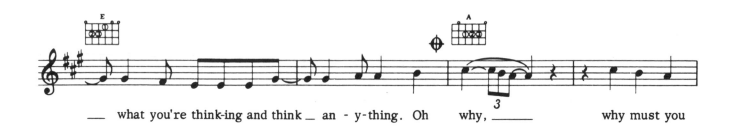

__ what you're think-ing and think __ an - y-thing. Oh why, _____ why must you

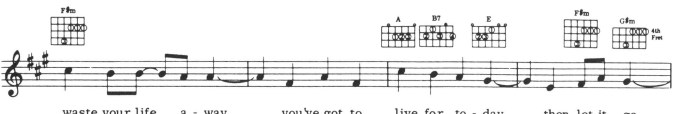

waste your life__ a - way, _____ you've got to live for to - day, __ then let it go. __

__ Oh __ lov-er, I want to spend this

time with __ you, _____ there's no-thing I would - n't do _____

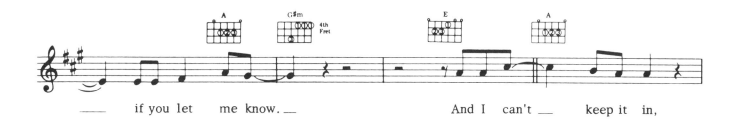

_____ if you let me know. __ And I can't __ keep it in,

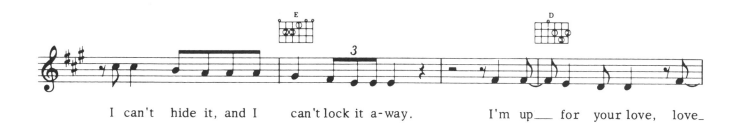

I can't hide it, and I can't lock it a-way. I'm up__ for your love, love__

__ heats my blood, blood spins my head and my head __ falls in love, oh.

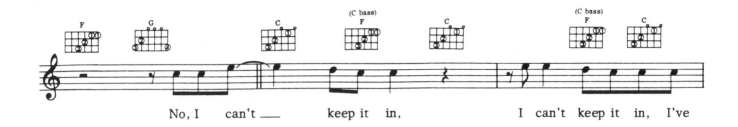

No, I can't __ keep it in, I can't keep it in, I've

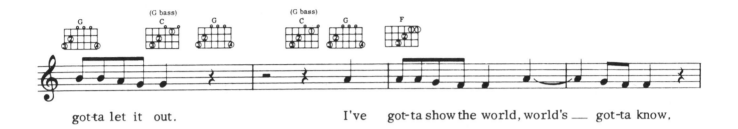

got-ta let it out. I've got-ta show the world, world's __ got-ta know,

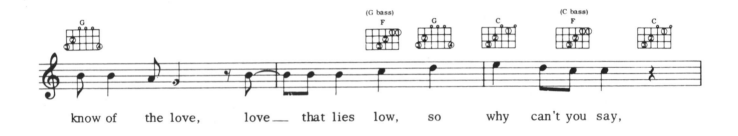

know of the love, love __ that lies low, so why can't you say,

if you know, then why can't you say? You've got too much de-ceit, de-ceit __

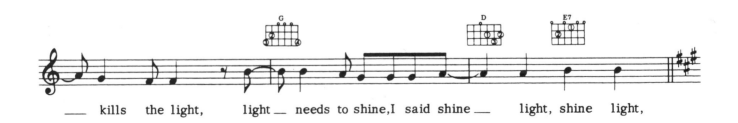

__ kills the light, light __ needs to shine, I said shine __ light, shine light,

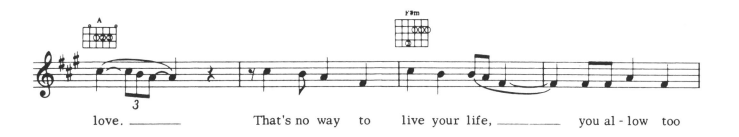

love. _____ That's no way to live your life, _____ you al-low too

much to go by, _____ and that won't do, _____ no ____

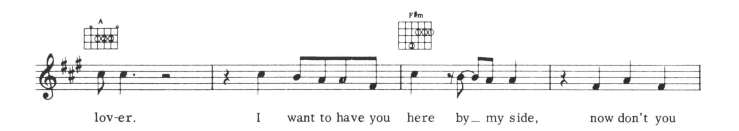

lov-er. I want to have you here by_ my side, now don't you

D. % al ⊕

run, don't you hide _____ while I'm with you. ___ An' I ___

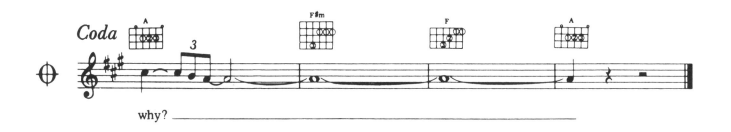

why? _____

Evil Woman

Words and music by Jeff Lynne

2. Rolled in from another town,
   Hit some gold too hot to settle down,
   But a fool and his money soon go separate ways,
   And you found a fool lyin' in a daze.

   Ha ha woman what you gonna do,
   You destroyed all the virtues that the Lord gave you,
   It's so good that you're feelin' pain
   But you better get your face on board the very next train. *(Chorus)*

3. Evil woman how you done me wrong,
   But now you're tryin' to wail a different song,
   Ha ha funny how you broke me up,
   You made the wine now you drink a cup.

   I came runnin' every time you cried,
   Thought I saw love smilin' in your eyes,
   Ha ha very nice to know
   That you ain't got no place left to go. *(Chorus)*

Strange Magic

Words and music by Jeff Lynne

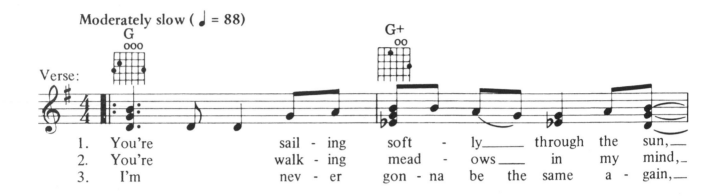

Verse:

1. You're sail - ing soft - ly____ through the sun,____
2. You're walk - ing mead - ows____ in my mind,
3. I'm nev - er gon - na be the same a - gain,____

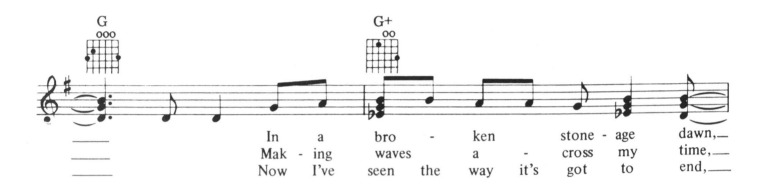

____ In a bro - ken stone - age dawn,____
____ Mak - ing waves a - cross my time,____
____ Now I've seen the way it's got to end,____

Chorus:

____ You fly____ so high. ____ I get a
____ Oh no,____ oh no. ____ I get a
____ Sweet dream,____ sweet dream. ____

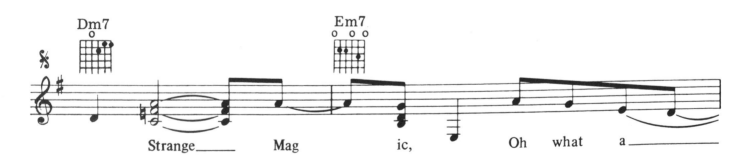

Strange____ Mag ic, Oh what a ____

Strange___ Mag - ic, Oh, it's a _____ Strange___ Mag-

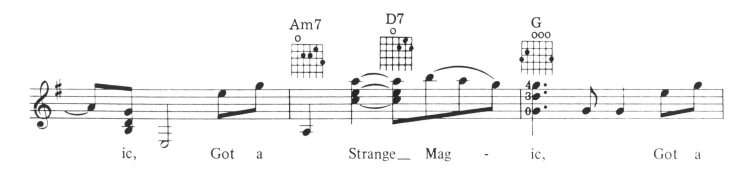

ic, Got a Strange___ Mag - ic, Got a

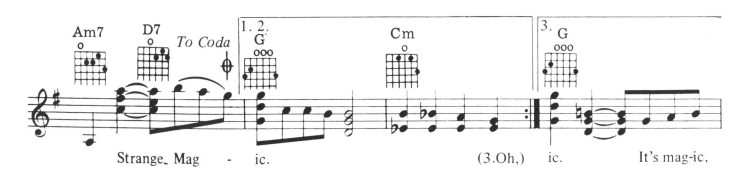

Strange___ Mag - ic. (3.Oh,) ic. It's mag-ic,

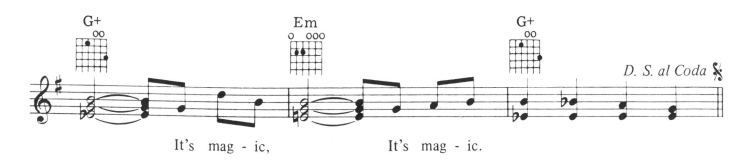

It's mag - ic, It's mag - ic.

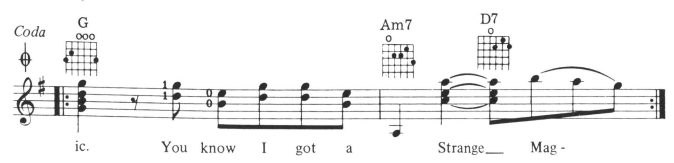

ic. You know I got a Strange___ Mag-

179

Daniel

Words and music by Elton John and Bernie Taupin

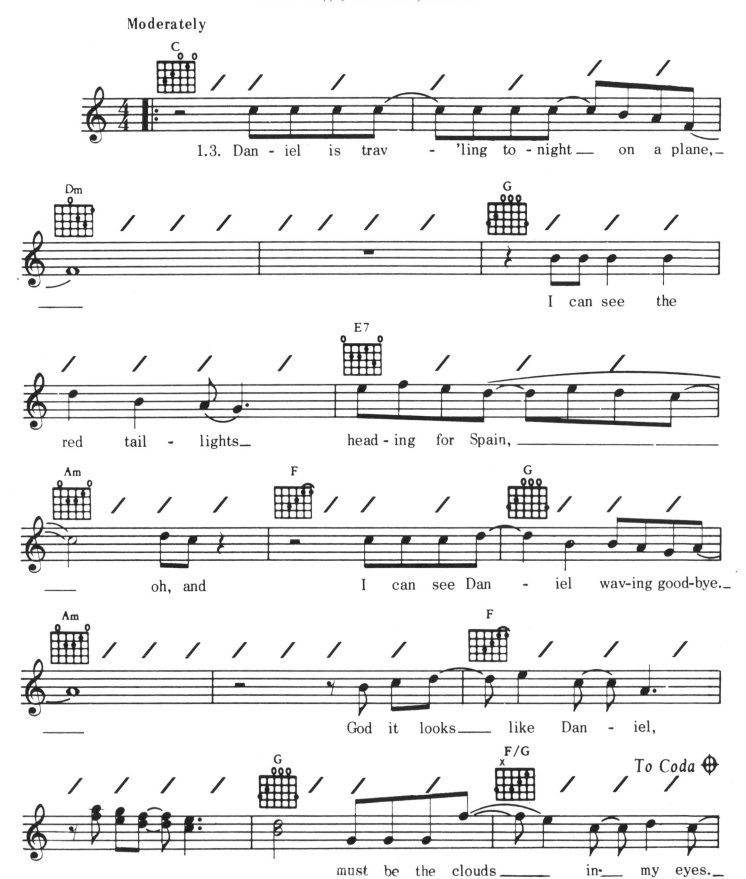

2. They say Spain is pretty, though I've never been,
   Well Daniel says it's the best place he's ever seen,
   Oh and he should know he's been there enough,
   Lord I miss Daniel, oh I miss him so much.

Only Sixteen

Words and music by Sam Cooke

Moderate

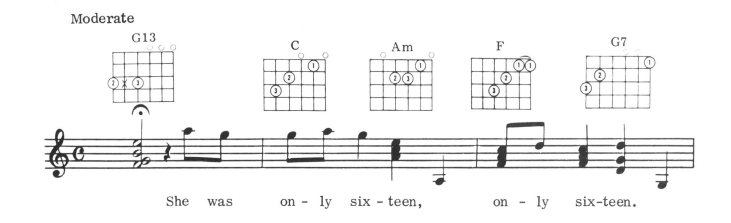

She was on-ly six-teen, on-ly six-teen.

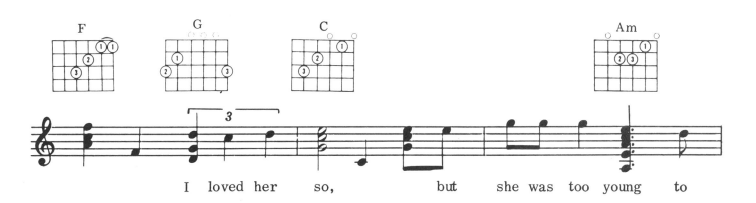

I loved her so, but she was too young to

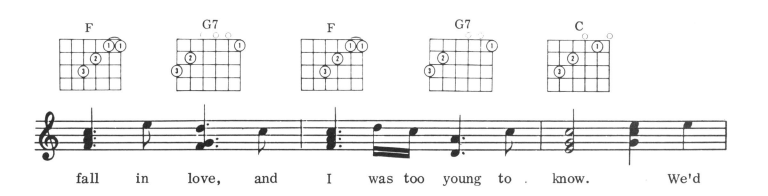

fall in love, and I was too young to know. We'd

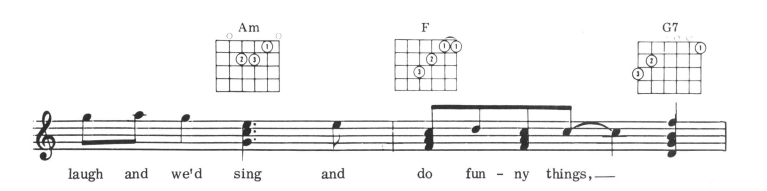

laugh and we'd sing and do fun-ny things, —

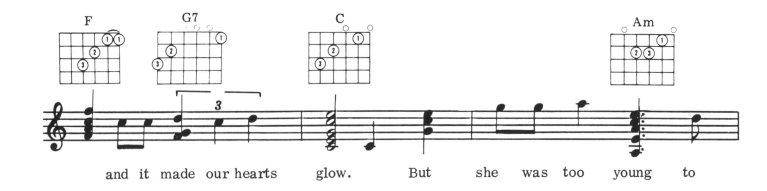

and it made our hearts glow. But she was too young to

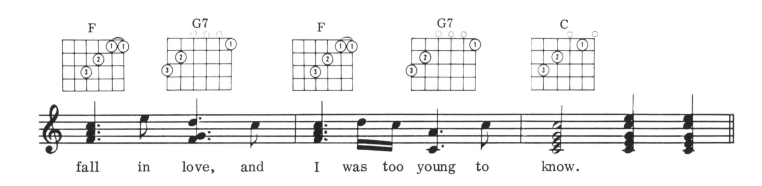

fall in love, and I was too young to know.

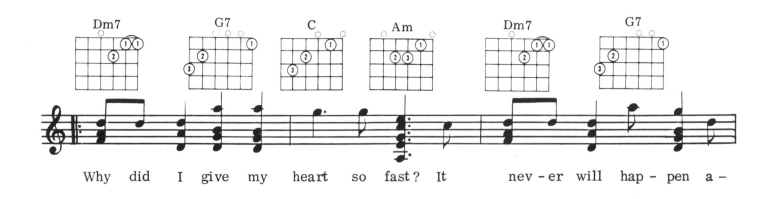

Why did I give my heart so fast? It nev-er will hap-pen a-

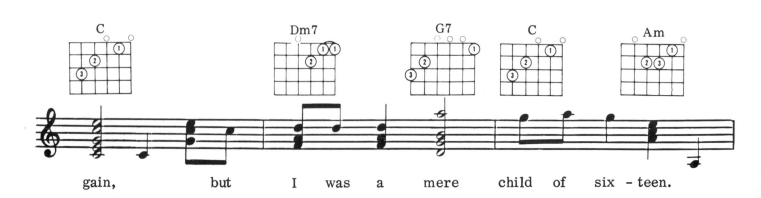

gain, but I was a mere child of six-teen.

I've aged a year since then. She was on - ly six - teen,

on - ly six - teen, { with eyes that would glow, but I loved that girl so, } but

she was too young to fall in love, and I was too young to

1. know. Then 2. know. But she was too young to

Repeat and fade

fall in love and I was too young to know.

Goodbye Yellow Brick Road

Words and music by Elton John and Bernie Taupin

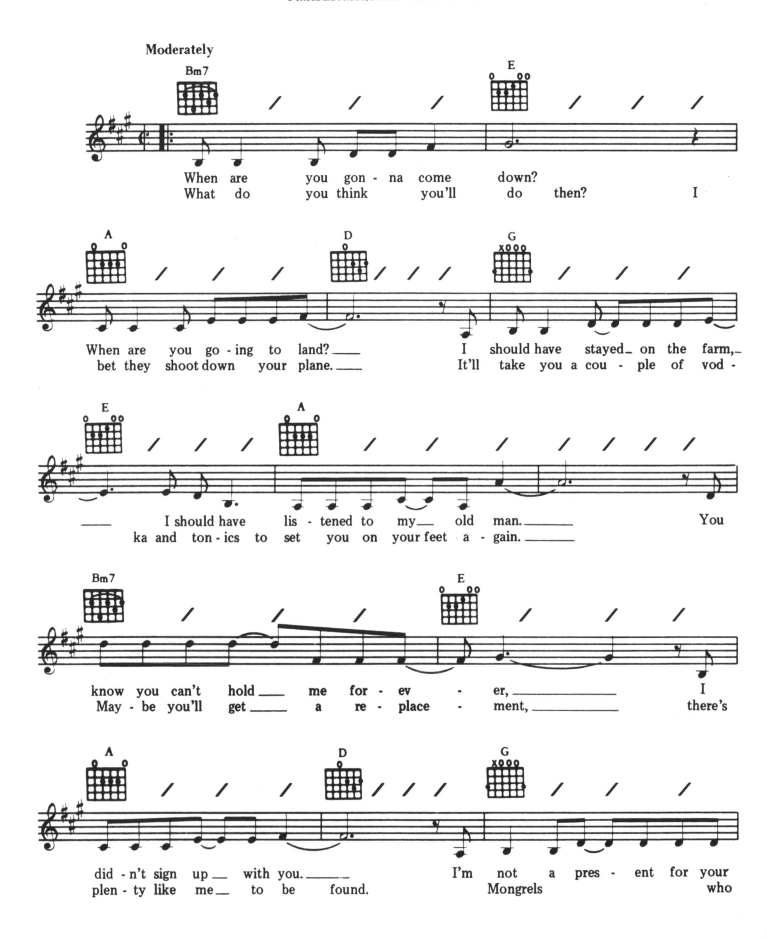

Moderately

When are you gon - na come down?
What do you think you'll do then? I

When are you go - ing to land? ___ I should have stayed_ on the farm, ___
bet they shoot down your plane. ___ It'll take you a cou - ple of vod -

___ I should have lis - tened to my_ old man. _____ You
ka and ton - ics to set you on your feet a - gain. _____

know you can't hold ___ me for - ev - er, _____ I
May - be you'll get ___ a re - place - ment, _____ there's

did - n't sign up ___ with you. _____ I'm not a pres - ent for your
plen - ty like me_ to be found. Mongrels who

owl in the woods, — hunt - ing the horn - y back

toad. Oh, I've fi - n'lly de - cid - ed my

fu - ture lies be - yond the yel - low brick

road. _____ Ah, _____

_____ ah. _____

Leaving On A Jet Plane

Words and music by John Denver

Chorus

don't know when I'll be back a-gain,___ Oh, babe, I hate to

1. 2.
go._____ 2. There's so
3. _____

3.
go._____ I'm leav - in' on a jet__ plane,

don't know when I'll be back__ a - gain,___ Oh,

babe,_____ I hate to go._____

(hold)

Saturday Night's Alright For Fighting

Words and music by Elton John and Bernie Taupin

had it with your dis - ci - pline.___ Oh, Sat - ur - day night's___ al -

right for fight - ing; get a lit - tle ac - tion in.

Get a - bout as oiled___ as a die - sel train,___ gon - na set this dance a -

light. 'Cause Sat - ur - day night's___ the night I like,

Sat - ur - day night's___ al - right, al - right, al - right,___ oo._____

Well, they're _____

Repeat and fade

Sat - ur - day, Sat - ur - day, Sat - ur - day, Sat - ur - day, Sat - ur - day, Sat - ur - day,

Sat - ur - day, Sat - ur - day, Sat - ur - day night's al - right.___

The Border Song

Words and music by Elton John and Bernie Taupin

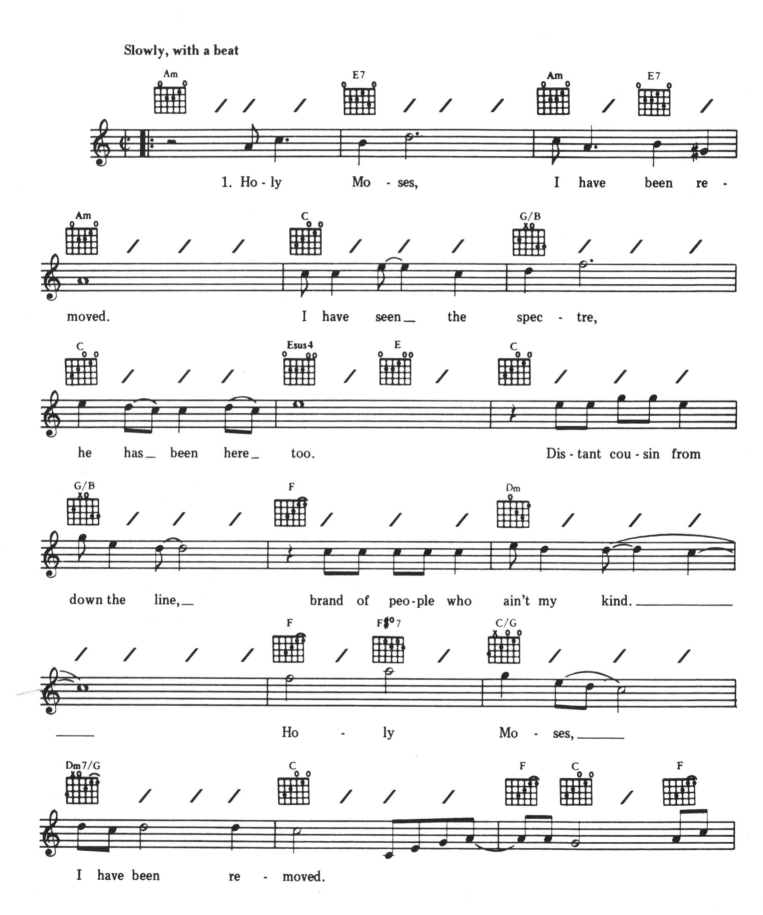

2. Holy Moses, I have been deceived.
   Now the wind has changed direction and I have to leave.
   Won't you please excuse my frankness, but it's not my cup óf tea.
   Holy Moses, I have been deceived.

3. Holy Moses, let us live in peace.
   Let us strive to find a way to make all hatred cease.
   There's a man over there. What's his color? I don't care.
   He's my brother, let us live in peace.

Heart Of Gold

Words and music by Neil Young

Summer Time Blues

Words and music by Eddie Cochran and Jerry Capehart

1. I'm a-gon-na raise a fuss, I'm a-gon-na raise a hol-ler,

A-bout a-work-in' all sum-mer just to try to earn a dol-lar,

Ev-'ry time I call my Ba-by,

Spoken Try to get a date, My Boss says, "No dice, Son, you got-ta work late"___

Sing Some-times I won-der what I'm a-gon-na do,___ But there

ain't no cure for the Sum-mer-time___ Blues.

2. A well my Mom 'n' Pa - pa told me, "Son, you
3. (I'm gon - na) take_ two_ weeks_ Gon - na

got - ta make some mo - ney,   If you
have a fine va - ca - tion,   I'm gon - na

want - ta use the car to go a rid - in' next_ Sun - day,"
take_ my_ prob - lem to the U - ni - ted Na - tions!

Spoken

Well, I did - n't go to work_ Told the Boss I was sick_ "Now you
Well, I called_ my_ Con - gress-man and He_ said (quote) "I'd_

Sing

can't_ use the car 'cause you did - n't work a lick"_____ Some-times I won-der what
like to help you, Son, but you're too young_ to vote"_____

I'm a - gon - na do, _ But there ain't no cure for the Sum-mer - time_ Blues.

1.

2.

3. I'm gon - na

199

C'mon Everybody

Words and music by Jerry Capehart and Eddie Cochran

1. Well, C'm - on, ev - 'ry - bod - y, And
2. (Well, my) ba - by's num - ber one, ___ But I'm
3. (Well, we'll) real - ly have a part - y, But we

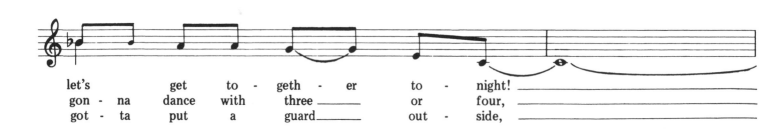

let's get to - geth - er to - night! ___
gon - na dance with three ___ or four, ___
got - ta put a guard ___ out - side, ___

___ I got some mon - ey in my jeans And I'm
And the house - 'll be ___ shak - in' From my
If the folks ___ come home I'm a -

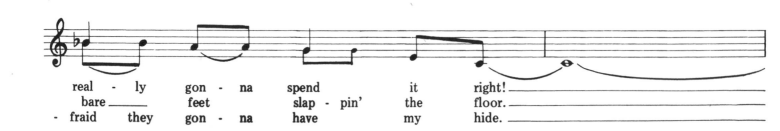

real - ly gon - na spend it right!
bare ___ feet slap - pin' the floor.
- fraid they gon - na have my hide.

F

Been a do - in' my home work
When you hear _____ that mus - ic you
There'll be no _____ more mov - ies for a

G7   F

all week long, Now the house is emp - ty, the
just can't sit still. If your broth - er won't rock then your
week or two; No more run - nin' a - round with the

G7   *(Shout)*

folks are gone. *Oo, oo!*
sis - ter will. *Oo, oo!* C'm
us - u - al crew. *Who cares.*

C   F   G7   C

- on, ev - 'ry - bod - y!

1 & 2   3

F   G7   C   C

2. Well, my
3. Well, we'll

Three Steps To Heaven
Words and music by Bob and Eddie Cochran

Now there are three ___ steps to Hea - ven, ___ Just

form - u - la for Hea-ven's ve - ry sim - ple, ___ Just

lis - ten and you will ___ plain - ly see. ___ And

fol - low the rules ___ and you will see. ___

as life tra - vels on, And things do go wrong, Just

fol - low steps one, two and three. ___

Step one ___ you find a girl ___ to ___ love. ___

Step two ___ she falls in love ___ with you. ___

Step three ___ you kiss And hold her tight - ly, ___ Yeah! that

sure seems like Hea - ven to ___ me.

The me. ___ Just fol - low

steps one, two and three.

203

Can't Smile Without You

Words and music by Chris Arnold, David Martin and Geoff Morrow

Coda

Bm7 — some peo-ple say___ hap-pi-ness takes___

E11 — so___ ver-y long to find.___

Amaj7 — ___

Am(maj7) — Well, I'm find-ing it hard___ leav-ing your love be-hind___

B7sus4 — ___

C7sus4 — me.

Repeat and fade

F — And you see, I can't smile with-out you.
(you.)___ *(Instrumental till fade.)*

Dm — I can't smile with-out you.

Gm — I can't laugh and I can't sing. I'm

C11 — find-ing it hard to do an-y-thing.___ You see I feel glad when

F —

Dm — you're glad. I feel sad when you're sad. If you___ on-ly knew what

Gm —

C11 — I'm___ go-ing through: I just can't smile with-out

Tryin' To Get The Feeling Aain

Words and music by David Pomeranz

made me shiv - er, made my knees start to quiv - er ev - 'ry time she walked

in. And I've looked high, low, ev - 'ry-where I pos - si - bly

can, but there's no try'n' to get the feel - ing a -

gain. It seemed to dis - ap - pear as fast as it came.

I've been up, down, _____ try'n' to get the feel - ing, I've been

up, down, _____ try'n' to get the feel - ing a - gain.

I'm A Believer

Words and music by Neil Diamond

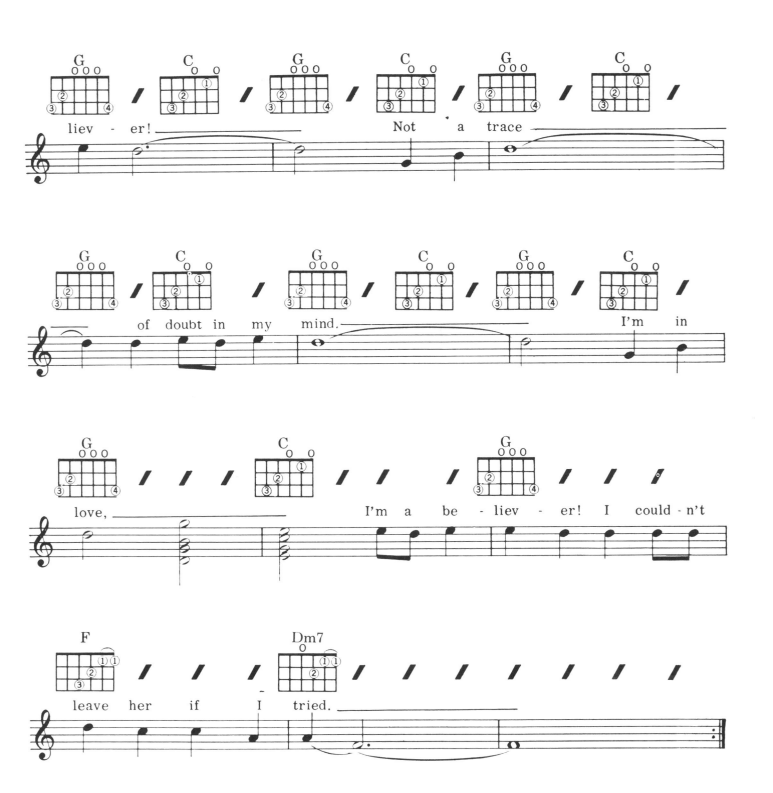

2. I thought love was more or less a givin' thing,
   Seems the more I gave the less I got.
   What's the use in tryin'? All you get is pain
   When I needed sunshine I got rain.

Everybody Knows This Is Nowhere

Words and music by Neil Young

Moderate Country style

I think I'd like to go___ back home___ and take it
Ev - 'ry time I think about back home___ it's cool and

eas - y. There's a wom- an that I'd like to get to know___
breez - y. I wish that I could be___ there right now,___

a - liv - ing there. }
just pass - ing time. }

Ev -'ry-bod-y seems to

won - der _____ what it's like down___ here. _____ I

got - ta get a - way from this day - to - day run-nin' a - round. Ev -'ry-bod - y

knows this is no - where. La la la la la la la.

Ev -'ry-bod-y, ev-'ry-bod-y knows.___ La la la la la la la la. _____

Repeat and fade

La la la la la la la la. _____

210

Interstellar Overdrive

Words and music by Syd Barrett, Nicholas Mason,
Roger Waters and Richard Wright

A Day In The Life
Words and music by John Lennon and Paul McCartney

It's Only Rock 'N' Roll

Words and music by Mick Jagger and Keith Richard

If I could stick__ my pen__ in my heart __ I'd
__ I could stick__ a knife__ in my heart _____

spill it all ov-er the stage _____ _____ it sat-is-fy ya or
su-i-cide right on the stage _____ Would__ it be e-nough for your

would it slide on by ya or would you think this boy is strange____ Ain't he stra-
teen-age lust would__ it help ease the pain_____ ease your brain

-- ya - yange if __ I could win__ you if __ I could sing__ you a __
_____ if __ I could dig __ down deep __ in my heart __ feel -

love song so di - vine_____ would __ it be e-nough for your
-ings would flood __ on the page_____ would __ it sat-is-fy ya would

215

_____ cheat-ing heart _____ If _____ I broke down and cried _____ if I cried
_____ it slide on by ya would _____ you think the boy's in - sane _____ he's in - sa—

_____ yi - yied.
_____ ya - yane I said I know _____ it's on - ly rock and roll but I

like it _____ I said I know _____ it's on - ly rock and roll but I

like it like it yes I do _____ Well I like it oh yes I

like it I like it I said

can't you see _____ this old boy's get-ting lone-ly If I _____

yes I do___ don't you think that you're the on-ly girl a-round_____

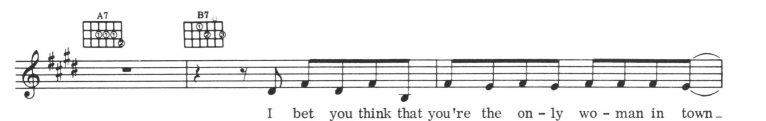

I bet you think that you're the on - ly wo - man in town_

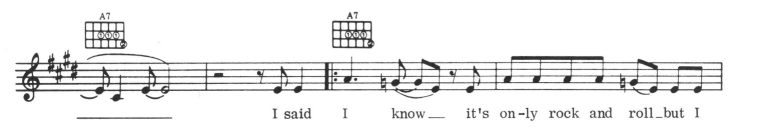

_____ I said I know___ it's on-ly rock and roll_but I

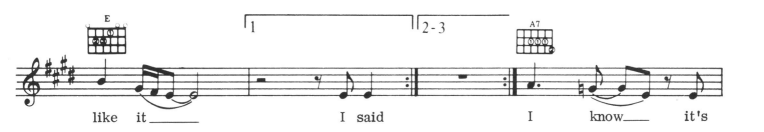

like it_____ I said I know___ it's

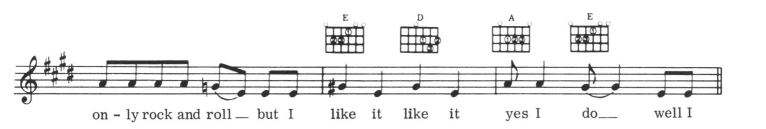

on - ly rock and roll ___ but I like it like it yes I do___ well I

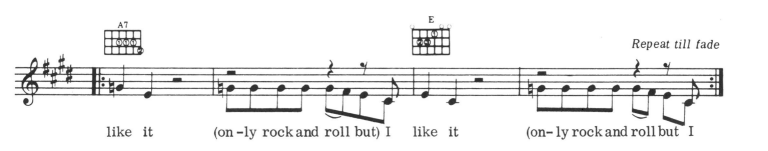

Repeat till fade

like it (on - ly rock and roll but) I like it (on - ly rock and roll but I

Paint It Black

Words and music by Mick Jagger and Keith Richard

Ruby Tuesday

Words and music by Mick Jagger and Keith Richard

She would nev-er say where she came from___
ques-tion why she needs to be so free___
There's no time to lose I heard her say___ she'll

Yes-ter-day___ don't matter if it's gone___ While the sun is bright___
Tell you its___ the on-ly way to be___ She just cant be chained
cash your dreams be - fore they slip a-way___ Dy-ing all the time

___ or in the dark-est night___ No one knows,
___ to a life where noth-ing's gained___ And nothing's lost___
___ lose your dreams and you___ will lose your mind___

CHORUS

she comes and goes.___
at such a cost.___
Ain't life un - kind.___

Good - bye Ru- by Tues - day

Who could hang a name___ on you___ When you change with ev - 'ry new day

to Coda ⊕   ⊕ **CODA**
Last time
D.S. al Coda

Still I'm gon-na miss you.   2. Don't

Angie

Words and music by Mick Jagger and Keith Richard

D.S. al Coda

you can't say___ we nev-er tried___
where will it___ lead us from here___
ain't it time___ we said good-bye___

⊕ CODA

An - gie___ I still love you ba - by___

Ev-'rywhere I look___ I see your eyes___ There ain't a woman that___comes

close to you Come on ba - by dry your eyes___ But

An - gie___ An - gie Ain't it good___ to be a - live___
An - gie___ An - gie They can't say___ we nev-er tried.

1

2

221

Astronomy Domine
Words and music by Syd Barrett

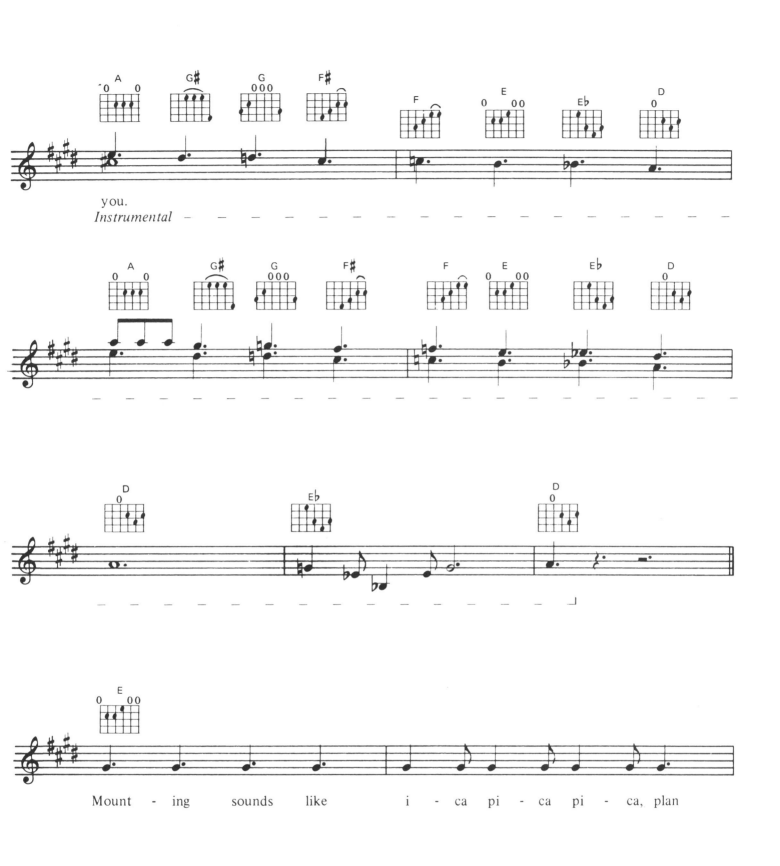

you.
Instrumental – – – – – – – – – – – – –

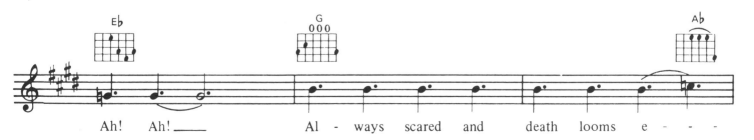

Mount - ing   sounds   like   i - ca   pi - ca   pi - ca,   plan

Ah!   Ah!___   Al - ways   scared   and   death   looms   e - -

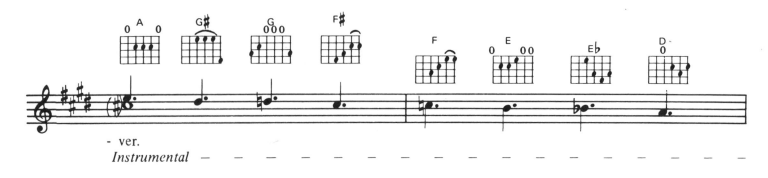

- ver.

Instrumental — — — — — — — — — — —

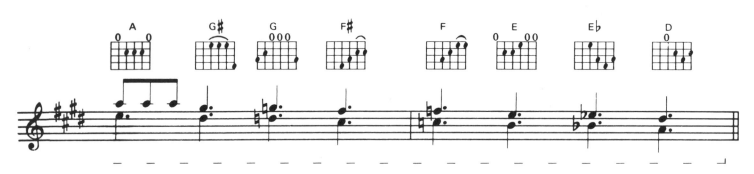

— — — — — — — — — — — — — —

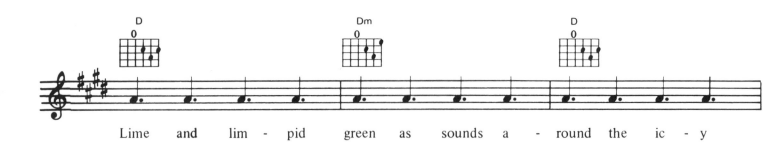

Lime and lim - pid green as sounds a - round the ic - y

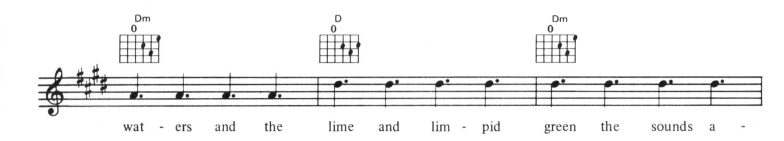

wat - ers and the lime and lim - pid green the sounds a -

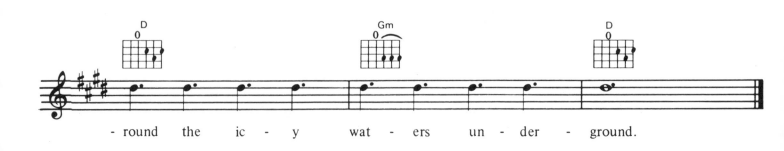

- round the ic - y wat - ers un - der - ground.

224

I've Got A Feeling

Words and music by John Lennon and Paul McCartney

Coda

Ev-'ry-bod-y had a hard year,   ev-'ry-bod-y had a
Ev-'ry-bod-y had a good year,   ev-'ry-bod-y let their

good time,   ev-'ry-bod-y had a wet dream,   ev-'ry-bod-y saw the
hair down,   ev-'ry-bod-y pulled-their socks up,   ev-'ry-bod-y put their

sun shine,   } , oh   yeah,   oh yeah,   oh   yeah.
foot down,

ad lib. "I've got a feeling" *etc.*

Play six times

Oh please believe me I'd hate to miss the train, oh yeah, oh yeah,
And if you leave me I won't be late again, oh no, oh no, oh no.
Yeah, Yeah, I've got a feeling, yeah!

I've got a feeling that keeps me on my toes, oh yeah, oh yeah.
I've got a feeling, I think that everybody knows, oh yeah, oh yeah, oh yeah.
Yeah, Yeah, I've got a feeling yeah!

Happy

Words and music by Mick Jagger and Keith Richard

Moderate Rock
VERSE

Well I nev - er kept a dol -lar past sun - set, it al -

- ways burned a hole in my pants. _____ Nev - er made a school mama hap-

- py, nev - er blew a sec -ond chance. _

CHORUS

I need a love _ to keep me hap -py, I need a __ love to

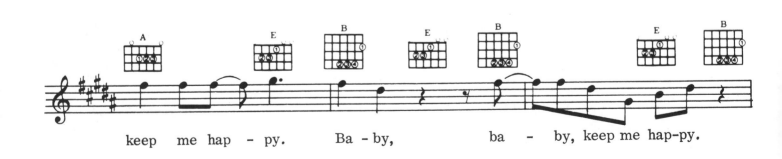

keep me hap - py. Ba - by, ba - by, keep me hap-py.

Ba - by, ba - by, keep me happy. Al - ways took can-dy from stran-

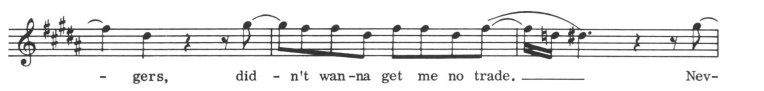

- gers, did - n't wan -na get me no trade. _____ Nev-

- er want to be like pa - pa, work - ing for the boss ev - 'ry

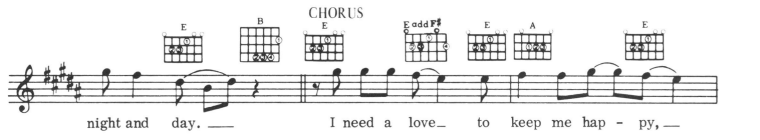

night and day. ___ I need a love_ to keep me hap - py, __

I need a love_ to keep me hap-py. Ba - by, ba -

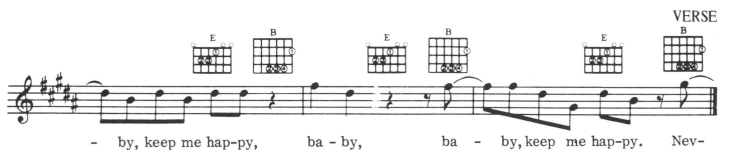

- by, keep me hap-py, ba - by, ba - by, keep me hap-py. Nev-

Big Bargain

ailable from all good music shops.

The bigger the book, the better the value.

Bumper Books

Show Tunes.
100 Hits for All Keyboards.
Arranged by Daniel Scott.
The songs that stopped the
shows, arranged for all
keyboards. Each song
includes chord symbols,
lyrics, performance tips
and suggested
registrations.
260pp, AM 74105

"The Ultimate Keyboard Book"
250 All-Time Hits.
A wonderful collection of
melodies for all keyboard
players. Complete with
registrations, lyrics and
chord symbols.
144pp, AM 63256
140pp, Book 2: AM 69212

250 All-Time Hits Book 3
A third collection of all-time
great songs arranged for all
keyboard players.
Complete with melody
lines, registrations and
chord symbols.
156pp, AM 80359

200 All-Time Show Tunes
A bumper collection of the
greatest show music, all
presented in easy to play
top line arrangements,
complete with lyrics and
chord symbols. Titles
include 'Consider Yourself',
'I Could Have Danced All
Night', 'Ol' Man River' and
'Sunrise, Sunset'.
148pp, AM 78643

101 Bumper SFX
For All Home Keyboards
A superb collection of 101
songs in many styles, all
arranged in letter-note SFX
notation. Complete with
suggested registrations
and lyrics.
300pp, AM 78908

100 Jazz & Blues Greats
One hundred of the world's
favourite jazz and blues
classics. Arranged for
piano/vocal with full lyrics
and chord symbols.
312pp, AM66614

In case of difficulty, please conta
Music Sales Limited, Newmarket Road, Bury St Edmunds, Suffolk IP33 3
Telephone: 0284 7026

Bringing you the world's best musi